11+
Verbal Reasoi

GL & Other Styles

TESTBOOK **6**

Standard & Multiple-choice 30 Minute Tests

Dr Stephen C Curran

Edited by Autumn McMahon

This book belongs to

ae®
PUBLICATIONS

Accelerated Education Publications Ltd

Guidance notes for parents

These practice papers can be completed as standard or multiple-choice tests.

Multiple-choice Tests

Answers are entered onto the answer sheets at the back of the book. The actual test would be marked by a computer but, for the purposes of these practice tests, you will need to mark it yourself. It is important for your child to treat it like the real thing and record an answer in the appropriate box by drawing a clear line through their chosen box with a pencil. Mistakes should be carefully rubbed out and not crossed out since in the actual test this would not be correctly recorded by the computer.

Standard Tests

Ask your child to fill in all the answers in the spaces as instructed in each section. Mistakes should be crossed through with a single line and the correct answer written clearly.

Marking and Feedback

The answers are provided at the back of this book. Only these answers are allowed. One mark should be given for each correct answer. Do not deduct marks for wrong answers. Do not allow half marks or 'the benefit of the doubt', as this might mask a child's need for extra help in the topic and does not replicate the real exam conditions. Always try to be positive and encouraging. Talk through any mistakes with your child and work out together how to arrive at the right answer.

Score	%	Score	%	Score	%	Score	%	Score	%
1	2%	11	22%	21	42%	31	62%	41	82%
2	4%	12	24%	22	44%	32	64%	42	84%
3	6%	13	26%	23	46%	33	66%	43	86%
4	8%	14	28%	24	48%	34	68%	44	88%
5	10%	15	30%	25	50%	35	70%	45	90%
6	12%	16	32%	26	52%	36	72%	46	92%
7	14%	17	34%	27	54%	37	74%	47	94%
8	16%	18	36%	28	56%	38	76%	48	96%
9	18%	19	38%	29	58%	39	78%	49	98%
10	20%	20	40%	30	60%	40	80%	50	100%

Verbal Reasoning Test 1

In these questions, the **same** letter will fit into **both** sets of brackets, to end the word in front of the brackets and start the word after the brackets.

Example:

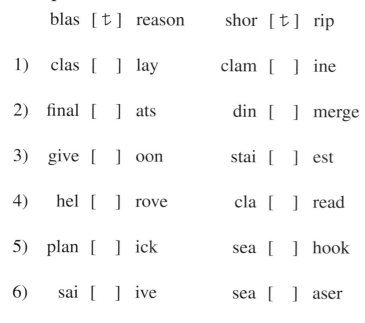

blas [t] reason   shor [t] rip

1)   clas [   ] lay   clam [   ] ine

2)   final [   ] ats   din [   ] merge

3)   give [   ] oon   stai [   ] est

4)   hel [   ] rove   cla [   ] read

5)   plan [   ] ick   sea [   ] hook

6)   sai [   ] ive   sea [   ] aser

In these questions, three of the five words are connected in some way. Find the **two** words that **do not** go with these three.

Example:

Monday Tuesday Friday midnight noon   _midnight_ and ____noon____

7) march August walk run swim   _____ and _____

8) damp moist dry drink wet   _____ and _____

9) calm neat cool warm placid   _____ and _____

10) locate look find discover lost   _____ and _____

11) jolly angry annoyed happy cheerful   _____ and _____

12) smart clever stupid understand intelligent   _____ and _____

In each question, find the next number in the sequence and write it in the brackets.

Example:

5 10 15 20 25 (30)

13) 1 2 4 7 11 (   )

14) 7 5 6 4 5 3 (   )

15) 3 6 12 24 48 (   )

16) 16 8 24 12 36 (   )

17) 3 9 4 16 5 25 6 (   )

18) 31 25 35 29 39 33 (   )

In these questions letters stand for numbers. Work out the answer to the sum, find its letter and write it in the brackets.

Example:

If **A = 2, B = 3, C = 4, D = 5** and **E = 1,**

what is the answer to this sum, **written as a letter**?

A + B − E = [C]

19) If **A = 4, B = 8, C = 9, D = 12** and **E = 18,**
    what is the answer to this sum, **written as a letter**?
    B × C ÷ E = [   ]

20) If **A = 3, B = 5, C = 6, D = 9** and **E = 11,**
    what is the answer to this sum, **written as a letter**?
    A + E − B = [   ]

21) If **A = 2, B = 6, C = 4, D = 8** and **E = 12,**
    what is the answer to this sum, **written as a letter**?
    E × A − D − C = [   ]

22) If **A = 20, B = 10, C = 4, D = 5** and **E = 2,**
    what is the answer to this sum, **written as a letter**?
    B × E ÷ C = [   ]

23) If **A = 3**, **B = 6**, **C = 7**, **D = 9** and **E = 11**,
   what is the answer to this sum, **written as a letter**?
   $A \times B - E = [\quad]$

24) If **A = 0**, **B = 9**, **C = 8**, **D = 2** and **E = 1**,
   what is the answer to this sum, **written as a letter**?
   $B \times A + C + E = [\quad]$

In these questions, underline **two** words, one from each group, that are closest in meaning.

Example:

(<u>sleep</u> run walk)   (smile laugh <u>snooze</u>)

25) (trip jump twist)   (snap dive stumble)

26) (team office task)   (force job cultivate)

27) (sun see sand)   (ocean castle view)

28) (undone unkind uncertain)   (indeed inhabit unfinished)

29) (plant occupy tempt)   (job journey inhabit)

30) (simple left wrong)   (write false right)

Read the following information then find the correct answer.

31) Three children have an amount of money between them. Angela has £5. Jason has one half of the total amount. Danny has £2 more than Angela.

   Which one of the following statements is true?   _____

   A. The children have £20 between them.
   B. Jason has the same amount as Angela.
   C. Danny has more than Jason.
   D. Jason and Danny have £19 between them.
   E. All three children have less than £7 each.

In these questions there are three pairs of words. The last pair of words is made up in the same way as the first two pairs. Find the missing word and write it in the brackets.

Example:

    (grind grin)   (fore for)   (piper [*pipe*])

32) (slime limes)   (stop tops)   (stone [   ])

33) (trams smart)   (bats stab)   (stop [   ])

34) (arrest star)   (ankle lean)   (state [   ])

35) (tears rates)   (steps pests)   (teams [   ])

36) (spoon son)   (beast bat)   (meant [   ])

37) (player real)   (flares seal)   (draped [   ])

Read the following information then find the two correct answers.

38) Frank, Betty, Aziz, Jessica and Mike work part-time in a burger bar.

    Aziz, Betty and Mike work for 2 hours on Monday.
    Jessica and Frank work for 4 hours on Tuesday.
    Aziz and Jessica work for 3 hours on Wednesday.
    Frank, Aziz and Mike work for 2 hours on Thursday.
    Betty and Frank work for 2 hours on Friday.
    Mike and Jessica work for 3 hours on Saturday.

    Which two people work the same number of hours?

    _____ and _____

In these sentences, a four-letter word can be found at the end of one word and the beginning of the next word. Find the two words that contain the hidden word and write it on the line.

Example:

    The pro<u>be st</u>reaked through outer space.   *best*

39) Food eaten today will cost half price.   _____

40) The team flies to Spain tomorrow.   _____

41) Rugby players often get serious injuries.   _____

42) The children were arranged in four classes.   _____

43) Grandfather fed the tame puffin every day.   _____

44) The fire alarm rang very loudly.   _____

In these questions, the word in the middle of the second group is made in the **same way** as the word in the middle of the first group. Find the word that is missing in the second group.

Example:

   (lint [liner] term)
   (drop [   ] even)   *drove*

45) (chest [cheer] great)
    (sport [   ] known)   _____

46) (least [trail] tired)
    (nears [   ] birch)   _____

47) (stain [slave] lever)
    (chill [   ] lambs)   _____

48) (today [toads] least)
    (child [   ] smart)   _____

49) (relate [darts] scored)
    (cuboid [   ] drills)   _____

50) (steam [leash] child)
    (chart [   ] chime)   _____

Score [   ] Percentage [%]

Verbal Reasoning Test 2

In these questions, one letter can be moved from the first word to the second word making two new words. The order of the letters must not be changed and the new words must make sense. Write the two new words or mark the letter that moves on your answer sheet.

Example:

	climb	lose	_limb_	_close_
1)	blame	tale	_____	_____
2)	fairy	earn	_____	_____
3)	least	vent	_____	_____
4)	cheat	fast	_____	_____
5)	planet	rust	_____	_____
6)	cable	rumble	_____	_____

In these sentences, the word in capitals has had **three** letters next to each other taken out. Find the word that is made from these letters without changing their order. The sentence that you make must make sense.

Example:

John bought a new COMER. COM**PUT**ER _PUT_

7) The chickens roamed around the FYARD. _____

8) A school is a place of LNING. _____

9) The food was SPED by too much salt. _____

10) Trains ran HLY from the local station. _____

11) The army ADCED into battle. _____

12) Smoke poured from the top of the VOLO. _____

In each question, find the missing number that will complete the question correctly.

Example:

$25 + 17 - 3 = 12 \times 3 + ?$ _3_

13) $3 \times 7 + 30 = 27 + ?$ _____

14) $9 \times 6 - 5 = 42 \div 6 \times ?$ _____

15) $60 \div 5 \times 2 = 40 \div 5 \times ?$ _____

16) $36 + 29 = 5 \times ?$ _____

17) $4 \times 13 + 11 = 6 \times 7 + ?$ _____

18) $19 \times 2 + 3 = 9 \times 6 - ?$ _____

A B C D E F G H I J K L M N O P Q R S T U V W X Y Z

The above alphabet is there to help you with these questions. Find the letters that complete each question in the best way.

Example:

DE is to FG as ST is to (UV)

19) GG is to JK as HI is to (   )

20) DW is to AZ as FV is to (   )

21) JN is to MK as HP is to (   )

22) JF is to NJ as TD is to (   )

23) DT is to JN as FR is to (   )

24) UQ is to WJ as TD is to (   )

In these questions, underline **two** words, one from each group, that have the most opposite meaning.

Example:

(<u>up</u> run walk)   (smile laugh <u>down</u>)

25) (succeed complete plan)   (fabricate fail fraction)

26) (forest damage damp)   (wash dry clean)

27) (multiply subtract divide)   (unite area measure)

28) (elevator ascend raise)   (lower descent escalator)

29) (thin deep crispy)   (fry meaning shallow)

30) (sit walk lead)   (follow tie clamp)

A B C D E F G H I J K L M N O P Q R S T U V W X Y Z

The above alphabet is there to help you with these questions. Each question has a different code. Work out the second code or word as instructed.

Example:

The code for TRAP is USBQ.
What is the word for DPME?   COLD

31) The code for TWELVE is RUCJTC.
What is the word for RFGPRW?   _____

32) The code for SCHOOL is TEKSTR.
Work out the code for PUPILS.   _____

33) The code for GHOST is CDKOP.
What is the word for OJWGA?   _____

34) The code for ADDITION is XGALQLLQ.
Work out the code for DIVISION.   _____

35) The code for NEVER is OCYAW.
What is the word for QYXOJ?   _____

36) The code for FACTORY is DDAWMUW.
Work out the code for OFFICES.   _____

Read the following information then find the correct answer.

37) Jim, Hugh and Tom all arrived at school at 8.45am. Hugh left home at 8.26am. Jim took 8 minutes longer than Tom to get to school. Tom took 18 mintues to get to school.

Which one of these statements is true? _____

A. Jim and Tom left home at the same time.
B. Tom arrived last.
C. Tom left home before Hugh.
D. Jim left home first.
E. Hugh and Tom left home before Jim.

Read the following information then find the correct answer.

38) Peter is twice as old as Thomas was last year. Sally is 8. Thomas is three years older than Sally was last year.

Using this information answer the following question.

How old is Peter? _____

In these questions, find one word from each pair of brackets that will complete the sentence in the best way. Underline **both** words.

Example:

Time is to (first, <u>second</u>, third) as distance is to (gram, kilo, <u>metre</u>)

39) Glance is to (lance, stare, smile) as flip is to (grab, jump, lip)

40) Angler is to (degree, right, rod) as cricketer is to (bat, white, run)

41) Stop is to (go, pots, post) as bats is to (bails, stab, belfry)

42) Pen is to (pencil, crayon, ink) as brush is to (broom, paint, clean)

43) Flute is to (blow, suck, play) as guitar is to (string, pluck, bow)

44) Letter is to (envelope, reply, word) as digit is to (finger, clock, number)

In these questions there are four words. Three of the words have been given a code. The codes are not written in the same order as the words and one code is missing.

CAST   SACK   TASK   TEAK

4279   8734   3789

45) Work out the code for STEAK.   _____

46) Work out the code for CASSETTE.   _____

47) What is the word for 39742?   _____

REST   STAR   SALT   TEAR

1456   4756   6714

48) Work out the code for SETTER.   _____

49) Work out the code for SEATS.   _____

50) What is the word for 67174?   _____

Score [ ]   **Percentage** [ ] **%**

Verbal Reasoning Test 3

In these questions, the **same** letter will fit into **both** sets of brackets, to end the word in front of the brackets and start the word after the brackets.

Example:

blas [t] reason   shor [t] rip

1) stee [ ] rain   swor [ ] ream

2) plan [ ] ating   fat [ ] dit

3) pani [ ] andle   magi [ ] all

4) stra [ ] ink   cla [ ] orse

5) clas [ ] eat   fis [ ] ope

6) radi [ ] uter   hal [ ] range

In these questions, three of the five words are connected in some way. Find the **two** words that **do not** go with these three.

Example:

Monday Tuesday Friday midnight noon   _midnight_ and _noon_

7) role butter soup cook sardine   _____ and _____

8) orange yellow banana pair violet   _____ and _____

9) France Australia Japan Germany Belgium   _____ and _____

10) base bottom top peak summit   _____ and _____

11) winner leader chief ruler protractor   _____ and _____

12) definite vague certain positive negative   _____ and _____

In each question, find the next number in the sequence and write it in the brackets.

Example:

    5   10   15   20   25   (30)

13) 15   17   20   24   29   (   )

14) 25   19   22   23   19   27   (   )

15) 3   6   12   24   (   )

16) 4   9   13   18   22   27   (   )

17) 4   8   10   20   22   (   )

18) 16   9   18   11   20   13   (   )

In each question, find the missing number that will complete the question correctly.

Example:

    $25 \times 17 - 3 = 12 \times 3 + ?$ _3_

19) $2 \times 25 + 16 = 49 + 37 - ?$ _____

20) $7 \times 5 - 13 = 5 \times 4 + ?$ _____

21) $65 \div 13 \times 9 = 5 \times 3 \times ?$ _____

22) $81 + 29 - 17 = 33 + 29 + ?$ _____

23) $7 \times 14 + 3 = 9 \times 9 + ?$ _____

24) $5 \times 3 + 23 = 7 \times 6 - ?$ _____

In these questions, find **one** word from **each** group that makes one correctly spelt word when joined together. The word from the first group always comes first. Underline **both** words.

Example:

       (<u>motor</u> gas electric)   (engine bus <u>cycle</u>)

25) (rat rut rot)   (ate eat feed)

26) (out in up)   (space stance square)

27) (deep tin can)   (not end nibble)

28) (meant man mean)   (hole over shone)

29) (call cast cost)   (flower member away)

30) (hour second time)   (furniture table chest)

Read the following information then find the correct answer.

31) Giles, Brenda and Dave go shopping for CDs. Each has £15 to spend.

     Giles buys a CD for £12. Dave buys a classical music CD for his grandma for £9. Brenda buys a CD and gets £3.50 in change.

     Which one of the following statements is true?   _____

     A. Brenda buys a CD for £12.
     B. Dave likes classical music.
     C. Giles spends more than Brenda.
     D. Giles gets £2 more in change than Dave.
     E. They spend £34.50 between them.

In these questions there are three pairs of words. The last pair of words is made up in the same way as the first two pairs. Find the missing word and write it in the brackets.

Example:

(grind grin)   (fore for)   (piper [*pipe*])

32) (reason nose)   (censor rose)   (stones [   ])

33) (lotto tool)   (range near)   (taste [   ])

34) (centred dent)   (funeral lane)   (sixteen [   ])

35) (brakes kerb)   (larder deal)   (pastry [   ])

36) (install tail)   (sorbets best)   (ailment [   ])

37) (relapse ears)   (praised ripe)   (cleaner [   ])

A B C D E F G H I J K L M N O P Q R S T U V W X Y Z

The above alphabet is there to help you with these questions. Find the next letters in the sequence and write them in the brackets.

Example:

AB   BC   CD   DE   EF   (*FG*)

38) DF   GI   JL   MO   PR   (   )

39) HI   LM   PQ   TU   (   )

40) HM   GK   II   HG   JE   (   )

41) MN   PQ   ST   VW   (   )

42) TT   TS   QR   QQ   (   )

43) WF   TG   VI   SL   UP   (   )

Read the following information then find the correct answer.

44) Peter, Mary, Julie, Harriet and James eat out at a restaurant.

Peter, Harriet and Mary order some fish and some chips.
James and Julie each order a burger.
Harriet and Julie order peas and carrots.
James and Mary order carrots and sprouts.
Mary and Julie order an ice cream.
Peter, Harriet and Mary each order a cola.
James orders a lemonade.

Who orders the most items? _____

In these questions there are two pairs of words. One of the five answers will go equally well with both pairs of words. Find the word.

Example:

(steady   firm)   (barn   shed)   _stable_

office   chain   beach   farm   stable

45) (shoot   launch)   (flame   blaze)   _____
    blast   inferno   fire   submerge   liftoff

46) (swan   bird)   (crouch   squat)   _____
    wings   duck   chicken   bend   sit

47) (descend   drop)   (bowl   basin)   _____
    fall   bath   sink   lose   throw

48) (money   currency)   (thump   crush)   _____
    cash   loot   smash   crash   pound

49) (right   accurate)   (amend   rectify)   _____
    true   write   change   correct   return

50) (sketch   design)   (equal   even)   _____
    colour   write   same   draw   paint

Score [   ] **Percentage** [%]

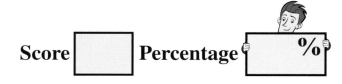

Verbal Reasoning Test 4

In these questions, one letter can be moved from the first word to the second word making two new words. The order of the letters must not be changed and the new words must make sense. Write the two new words or mark the letter that moves on your answer sheet.

Example:

	climb	lose	_limb_	_close_
1)	where	save	_____	_____
2)	beast	core	_____	_____
3)	bridge	ruby	_____	_____
4)	pearl	quit	_____	_____
5)	wheat	shin	_____	_____
6)	heard	gent	_____	_____

In these sentences, the word in capitals has had **three** letters next to each other taken out. Find the word that is made from these letters without changing their order. The sentence that you make must make sense.

Example:

John bought a new COMER. COMPUTER _PUT_

7) My dad likes MUSD with his meat. _____

8) The grass was a beautiful SE of green. _____

9) The CAULT was used to throw rocks into the castle. _____

10) The team to play in the match was chosen by the MAER. _____

11) The archaeologist found a SKEON in the ancient tomb. _____

12) Grandfather DED the old garden fence. _____

In these sentences, a four-letter word can be found at the end of one word and the beginning of the next word. Find the two words that contain the hidden word and write it on the line.

Example:

    The pro<u>be st</u>reaked through outer space.   _____*best*_____

13) Perfumes contain ice water from mountain springs.   _____

14) Her money fell from her open purse.   _____

15) The physician treated her patient's illnesses.   _____

16) The striker spun towards the goal.   _____

17) My kite might blow away today.   _____

18) Asking questions will improve your knowledge.   _____

A B C D E F G H I J K L M N O P Q R S T U V W X Y Z

The above alphabet is there to help you with these questions. Find the letters that complete each question in the best way.

Example:

    DE is to FG as ST is to (UV)

19) AC is to GI as KM is to (   )

20) KH is to SP as CZ is to (   )

21) YU is to AW as MI is to (   )

22) BY is to CX as DW is to (   )

23) LJ is to IM as RP is to (   )

24) DE is to HJ as PQ is to (   )

In these questions, the middle number in the last group is made up in the same way as the middle numbers in the first two groups. Find the missing number and write it in the brackets.

Example:

(5 [15] 10)   (8 [17] 9)   (10 [30] 20)

25) (10 [40] 15)   (8 [28] 10)   (6 [   ] 12)

26) (6 [10] 14)   (12 [17] 22)   (9 [   ] 23)

27) (6 [20] 12)   (10 [37] 25)   (10 [   ] 11)

28) (48 [29] 19)   (35 [26] 9)   (53 [   ] 17)

29) (7 [54] 8)   (8 [70] 9)   (12 [   ] 11)

30) (54 [95] 37)   (66 [97] 27)   (73 [   ] 29)

A B C D E F G H I J K L M N O P Q R S T U V W X Y Z

The above alphabet is there to help you with these questions. Each question has a different code. Work out the second code or word as instructed.

Example:

The code for TRAP is USBQ.
What is the word for DPME?   COLD

31) The code for CRIME is DTLQJ.
What is the word for QNDRJ?   _____

32) The code for SCIENCE is UEKGPEG.
Work out the code for ENGLISH.   _____

33) The code for BEST is CDTS.
What is the word for XNSRU?   _____

34) The code for REPLAY is TDRKCX.
What is the word for QQCMID?   _____

35) The code for FORTY is JSVXC.
What is the word for JMBIH?   _____

36) The code for BABY is DCDA.
What is the word for HCEG?   _____

Read the following information then find the correct answer.

37) Michelle, Sheila, John, Jenny and Freda all go to the same school.

Michelle is older than Sheila, but younger than Jenny. John is older than Freda, but younger than Sheila.

Who is the oldest? _____

38) Simon, Brenda, Alice and Jake have just been given their pocket money. Simon received twice as much as Brenda. Jake received £2 less than Alice who received £5 more than Simon. Jake received £7 in pocket money.

Which of the following statements is true? _____

A. Brenda received £4 in pocket money.
B. The four children received £20 between them.
C. The 2 girls received less than the 2 boys.
D. The boys received £11 between them.
E. Simon received the most pocket money.

In these questions letters stand for numbers. Work out the answer to the sum, find its letter and write it in the brackets.

Example:

If **A = 2, B = 3, C = 4, D = 5** and **E = 1**,
what is the answer to this sum, **written as a letter**?

A + B − E = [C **]**

39) If **A = 5, B = 10, C = 15, D = 20** and **E = 25**,
what is the answer to this sum, **written as a letter**?

E ÷ A + D − C = [   ]

40) If **A = 3, B = 6, C = 9, D = 10** and **E = 12**,
what is the answer to this sum, **written as a letter**?

B × D ÷ A − D = [   ]

41) If **A = 0, B = 2, C = 4, D = 8** and **E = 10**,
what is the answer to this sum, **written as a letter**?

E × A + B + D = [   ]

42) If **A = 20, B = 10, C = 4, D = 5** and **E = 2**,
what is the answer to this sum, **written as a letter**?

C × D ÷ B × D = [   ]

43) If **A = 32**, **B = 64**, **C = 2**, **D = 4** and **E = 16**,
 what is the answer to this sum, **written as a letter**?

 $C \times D \times C \times C = [\quad]$

44) If **A = 2**, **B = 15**, **C = 16**, **D = 12** and **E = 9**,
 what is the answer to this sum, **written as a letter**?

 $A \times E - D + E = [\quad]$

In these questions, underline **two** words, one from each group, that are closest in meaning.

Example:

    (<u>sleep</u> run walk)   (smile laugh <u>snooze</u>)

45) (hole part fraction)   (whole roll role)

46) (tree banana tear)   (leave split depart)

47) (deceitful disconnect delegate)   (dislike distrust dishonest)

48) (article appoint argue)   (retire disagree discharge)

49) (strand pine pullover)   (needle thread knit)

50) (darkness pair match)   (flame contest light)

Score [ ] Percentage [ ] %

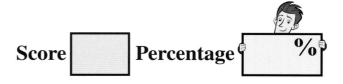

Verbal Reasoning Test 5

In these questions, the **same** letter will fit into **both** sets of brackets, to end the word in front of the brackets and start the word after the brackets.

Example:

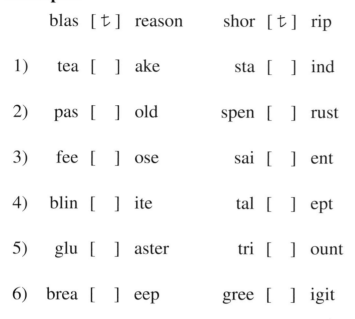

blas [t] reason   shor [t] rip

1)   tea [ ] ake   sta [ ] ind

2)   pas [ ] old   spen [ ] rust

3)   fee [ ] ose   sai [ ] ent

4)   blin [ ] ite   tal [ ] ept

5)   glu [ ] aster   tri [ ] ount

6)   brea [ ] eep   gree [ ] igit

In these sentences, a four-letter word can be found at the end of one word and the beginning of the next word. Find the two words that contain the hidden word and write it on the line.

Example:

The pro<u>be st</u>reaked through outer space.   _____*best*_____

7) The twins are about to enter.   _____

8) The town's defenders were local soldiers.   _____

9) Pains affect marathon runners' tired bodies.   _____

10) The tube station was under the ground.   _____

11) This leopard can run very quickly.   _____

12) Rain fell very early next morning.   _____

In each question, find the missing number that will complete the question correctly.

Example:

$25 + 17 - 3 = 12 \times 3 + ?$ ___3___

13) $120 \div 3 - 11 = 17 + 41 - ?$ _____

14) $5 \times 7 + 23 = 3 \times 9 + ?$ _____

15) $81 \div 9 \times 7 = 17 \times 3 + ?$ _____

16) $55 + 17 = 5 \times 12 + ?$ _____

17) $6 \times 11 + 18 = 3 \times 7 \times ?$ _____

18) $45 \div 9 + 28 = 120 \div 8 + ?$ _____

A B C D E F G H I J K L M N O P Q R S T U V W X Y Z

The above alphabet is there to help you with these questions. Find the next letters in the sequence and write them in the brackets.

Example:

| AB | BC | CD | DE | EF | (FG) |

19) DM   EL   GK   JJ   NI   (   )

20) SC   QD   OF   MI   (   )

21) VZ   WX   YV   ZT   BR   (   )

22) NM   OL   PK   QJ   (   )

23) RE   RB   OY   OV   LS   (   )

24) WG   TI   UK   RM   SO   (   )

In these questions there are four words. Three of the words have been given a code. The codes are not written in the same order as the words and one code is missing.

MICE   MACE   TAME   COAT

1256   5246   4321

25) Work out the code for TEAM.   _____

26) Work out the code for COME.   _____

27) What is the word for 5216?   _____

STEM   MAST   FLEA   SALE

9651   2876   5179

28) Work out the code for LEAST.   _____

29) Work out the code for MEALS.   _____

30) What is the word for 51769?   _____

Read the following information then find the correct answer.

31) Brenda, Sally and Gordon take the train from 3 different places back home to their house in Birmingham.

Gordon left at 8.35am and Sally 7 minutes later. It took Brenda $2\frac{1}{2}$ hours to make the trip, 20 minutes longer than Gordon who started 15 minutes before her. Sally arrived home at 10.40am.

At what time did the last person arrive home?   _____

In these questions, find one word from each pair of brackets that will complete the sentence in the best way. Underline **both** words.

Example:

Time is to (first, <u>second,</u> third) as distance is to (gram, kilo, <u>metre</u>)

32) Glass is to (shine, transparent, cracked) as wood is to (tree, strong, opaque)

33) Steel is to (metal, stainless, steal) as meet is to (welcome, meat, met)

34) Fly is to (insect, maggot, flew) as see is to (saw, sea, look)

35) Red is to (read, orange, stop) as green is to (sick, go, grass)

36) Nut is to (shell, crunch, cracking) as pea is to (soup, pod, bean)

37) Bee is to (honey, sting, hive) as fox is to (chicken, brush, den)

Read the following information then find the two correct answers.

38) Andrea, Barry, Mohammed, Kylie and Michelle each picked a selection of coloured paints for their pallets in an art class.

Andrea, Barry and Mohammed chose white and red.
Green was used by Michelle, Barry and Andrea.
Blue and purple were chosen by Mohammed, Michelle and Andrea.
Kylie used yellow, black and green.
Mohammed and Michelle chose yellow.
Barry and Kylie chose orange.

Which two people chose the most colours?

_____ and _____

In these questions, the word in the middle of the second group is made in the **same way** as the word in the middle of the first group. Find the word that is missing in the second group.

Example:

    (lint [liner] term)

    (drop [   ] even)   _____drove_____

39) (truce [score] chaos)

    (atlas [   ] event)   _____

40) (caper [place] plant)

    (medal [   ] track)   _____

41) (fried [grime] gloom)

    (alien [   ] solid)   _____

42) (prize [trace] cheat)

    (leave [   ] sound)   _____

43) (Santa [slant] Claus)

    (point [   ] craft)   _____

44) (glint [bring] amber)

    (prams [   ] visit)   _____

In these questions, find **one** word from **each** group that makes one correctly spelt word when joined together. The word from the first group always comes first. Underline **both** words.

Example:

    (<u>motor</u> gas electric)   (engine bus <u>cycle</u>)

45) (brush comb hair)   (an at in)

46) (low tall high)   (fall light din)

47) (friend enemy mate)   (boat liner ship)

48) (liner boat ship)   (enemy mate friend)

49) (sleep rest snore)   (ring iron ore)

50) (quiet loud shout)   (speaker lecturer teacher)

Score [   ]   **Percentage** [   ] **%**

Verbal Reasoning Test 6

In these questions, one letter can be moved from the first word to the second word making two new words. The order of the letters must not be changed and the new words must make sense. Write the two new words or mark the letter that moves on your answer sheet.

Example:

	climb	lose	_limb_ _close_
1)	stock	axis	_____ _____
2)	steam	pill	_____ _____
3)	range	crow	_____ _____
4)	crater	maker	_____ _____
5)	native	angle	_____ _____
6)	crack	miner	_____ _____

In these questions, three of the five words are connected in some way. Find the **two** words that **do not** go with these three.

Example:

Monday Tuesday Friday midnight noon _midnight_ and _noon_

7) smack bounce hit spring strike _____ and _____

8) cut slim trim chop fat _____ and _____

9) first aid assist medicine help _____ and _____

10) irregular abnormal usual unusual normal _____ and _____

11) imitate copy write draw mimic _____ and _____

12) money forgery fake copy appear _____ and _____

In each question, find the next number in the sequence and write it in the brackets.

Example:

      5   10   15   20   25 (*30*)

13) 1   4   9   12   17   20 (   )

14) 17   18   16   17   15   16 (   )

15) 2   2   4   12   48 (   )

16) 5   13   11   10   18   16   15 (   )

17) 13   20   14   17   15   14   16 (   )

18) 21   35   25   30   29   25 (   )

In each question, find the missing number that will complete the question correctly.

Example:

    $25 + 17 - 3 = 12 \times 3 + ?$ *3*

19) $8 \times 9 + 3 = 100 - 60 + ?$ _____

20) $7 \times 8 - 19 = 15 \times 4 - ?$ _____

21) $72 \div 4 \times 2 = 3 \times 3 \times ?$ _____

22) $4 \times 6 + 13 = 3 \times 9 + ?$ _____

23) $3 \times 14 + 18 = 150 \div 2 - ?$ _____

24) $45 \times 4 + 20 = 8 \times 5 \times ?$ _____

A B C D E F G H I J K L M N O P Q R S T U V W X Y Z

The above alphabet is there to help you with these questions. Find the letters that complete each question in the best way.

Example:

DE is to FG as ST is to (UV)

25) DT is to ES as FW is to (   )

26) GO is to NG as IE is to (   )

27) SW is to PA as LM is to (   )

28) DE is to BF as JH is to (   )

29) JJ is to EO as MN is to (   )

30) EA is to XX as DB is to (   )

Read the following information then find the correct answer.

31) Three children have an amount of money between them.

Sophie has £6. Charley has two-thirds of the total amount.
Tim has £3 more than Sophie.

Which of the following statement is true?   _____

A. The children have £40 between them.
B. Charley has the same amount as Sophie.
C. Charley has less than Tim.
D. Sophie and Tim have £15 between them.
E. All three children have less than £12 each.

In these questions there are three pairs of words. The last pair of words is made up in the same way as the first two pairs. Find the missing words and write it in the brackets.

Example:

    (grind grin)   (fore for)   (piper [*pipe*])

32) (trades dear)   (glared real)   (flames [   ])

33) (bases cases)   (might night)   (vest [   ])

34) (memory room)   (ninety teen)   (offers [   ])

35) (caterer cater)   (service serve)   (realism [   ])

36) (target rage)   (sister site)   (backer [   ])

37) (stable eats)   (enamel lane)   (parrot [   ])

Read the following information then find the two correct answers.

38) Saeeda, Harry, Nick, Katie and Michelle received lots of letters this week.

Nick, Harry and Michelle each received 3 letters on Monday.
Katie and Saeeda each received 2 letters on Tuesday.
Nick and Katie each received 4 letters on Wednesday.
Saeeda, Nick and Michelle each received 3 letters on Thursday.
Katie and Harry each received 1 letter on Friday.
Harry and Saeeda each received 3 letters on Saturday.

Which two people received the same number of letters in the week?

_____ and _____

In these questions, underline **two** words, one from each group, that are closest in meaning.

Example:

    (<u>sleep</u> run walk)   (smile laugh <u>snooze</u>)

39) (spotted striped coloured)   (blank seen scene)

40) (jump walk trot)   (leap spin swim)

41) (complete complicate complain)   (ending beginning finish)

42) (soap laundry brush)   (washing powder liquid)

43) (crook crop crock)   (shepherd rustler criminal)

44) (cube bucket box)   (spade sugar fight)

In these questions, the word in the middle of the second group is made in the **same way** as the word in the middle of the first group. Find the word that is missing in the second group.

Example:

    (lint [liner] term)

    (drop [   ] even)   <u> *drove* </u>

45) (cheat [trace] prime)

    (stand [   ] delve)   _____

46) (bright [great] tease)

    (brutal [   ] giant)   _____

47) (closed [slide] timed)

    (grocer [   ] diode)   _____

48) (cheeky [enact] plant)

    (video [   ] spire)   _____

49) (travel [there] teeth)

    (bikini [   ] water)   _____

50) (spain [panic] china)

    (vivid [   ] asian)   _____

Score [   ] **Percentage** [**%**]

Verbal Reasoning Test 7

In these questions, underline **two** words, one from each group, that have the most opposite meaning.

Example:

    (<u>up</u> run walk)   (smile laugh <u>down</u>)

1) (inside superior volume)   (surface exterior interior)

2) (dear deer mouse)   (cheep cheap cat)

3) (solid hard rough)   (difficult smooth shiny)

4) (backward upwards downward)   (inwards outward forward)

5) (wild dense overgrown)   (angry garden calm)

6) (push clamp shut)   (open close slam)

In these sentences, the word in capitals has had **three** letters next to each other taken out. Find the word that is made from these letters without changing their order. The sentence that you make must make sense.

Example:

    John bought a new COMER.   COM**PUT**ER   <u>PUT</u>

7) We won a COUT at the fair.   _____

8) The SIER wore a new uniform.   _____

9) They are SPING their holidays in Spain.   _____

10) The door had a sign that said PRIE.   _____

11) The local DER sold us the new car.   _____

12) The old road was very UNN.   _____

In these questions, the **same** letter will fit into **both** sets of brackets, to end the word in front of the brackets and start the word after the brackets.

Example:

        blas [t] reason   shor [t] rip

13)   pla [   ] ear   cla [   ] ine

14)   slic [   ] agle   cas [   ] vent

15)   line [   ] ace   stai [   ] est

16)   cro [   ] ill   sno [   ] ear

17)   scar [   ] ast   proo [   ] airy

18)   clu [   ] ooth   sla [   ] ase

In these questions letters stand for numbers. Work out the answer to the sum, find its letter and write it in the brackets.

Example:

If **A = 2, B = 3, C = 4, D = 5** and **E = 1**,

what is the answer to this sum, **written as a letter**?

A + B − E = [C]

19) If **A = 4, B = 8, C = 9, D = 2** and **E = 18**,

what is the answer to this sum, **written as a letter**?

A × C ÷ E = [   ]

20) If **A = 30, B = 45, C = 60, D = 75** and **E = 15**,

what is the answer to this sum, **written as a letter**?

E + D − A = [   ]

21) If **A = 20, B = 40, C = 60, D = 80** and **E = 120**,

what is the answer to this sum, **written as a letter**?

B + E − D − A = [   ]

22) If **A = 20**, **B = 10**, **C = 4**, **D = 5** and **E = 8**,
what is the answer to this sum, **written as a letter**?

$C \times B \div E + D$ = [   ]

23) If **A = 3**, **B = 6**, **C = 8**, **D = 10** and **E = 12**,
what is the answer to this sum, **written as a letter**?

$A \times C - B - C$ = [   ]

24) If **A = 1**, **B = 9**, **C = 8**, **D = 7** and **E = 10**,
what is the answer to this sum, **written as a letter**?

$A \times B + C - E$ = [   ]

In each question, find the next number in the sequence and write it in the brackets.

Example:

    5   10   15   20   25 (30)

25) 12 11 14 12 15 12 15 (   )

26) 17 15 16 14 15 13 (   )

27) 3 6 10 20 24 48 (   )

28) 19 17 16 14 13 (   )

29) 2 6 4 12 10 30 (   )

30) 38 33 29 24 20 15 (   )

A B C D E F G H I J K L M N O P Q R S T U V W X Y Z

The above alphabet is there to help you with these questions. Each question has a different code. Work out the second code or word as instructed.

Example:

The code for TRAP is USBQ.
What is the word for DPME?   <u>COLD</u>

31) The code for SECOND is UDENPC.
What is the word for OHPTVD?   _____

32) The code for READING is SGDHNTN.
Work out the code for WRITING.   _____

33) The code for TOAST is SMXOO.
What is the word for AJXIZ?   _____

34) The code for MASTER is NCTVFT.
Work out the code for SERVANT.   _____

35) The code for QUEUE is PVCWB.
What is the word for RMCGM?   _____

36) The code for BEDROOM is WZYMJJH.
Work out the word for KITCHEN.   _____

Read the following information then find the correct answer.

37) Barbara, Bernard, Bill, Bob and Betty are brothers and sisters.

Betty is older than Bob, but younger than Barbara. Bob is 8 years old. Bill is older than Barbara. Bernard is younger than Bob.

How many of the children are older than Bob?   _____

Read the following information then find the correct answer.

38) Mary, Nicola and Gavin swim for the local team.
    They all swim in a 100m backstroke race.
    Nicola's time is 2 minutes 13 seconds.
    Gavin swims faster than Nicola but slower than Mary.

    Which of the following statements is true?   _____

    A. Mary swims 100m in under two minutes.
    B. Gavin is the slowest of the three and finishes last.
    C. Nicola is the quickest of the three.
    D. Mary finishes in front of Nicola.
    E. Boys swim faster than girls.

In these questions, find one word from each pair of brackets that will complete the sentence in the best way. Underline both words.

Example:

    Time is to (first, second, third) as distance is to (gram, kilo, metre)

39) Stale is to (hard, rotten, fresh) as clean is to (polluted, washed, filtered)

40) Smile is to (happy, grin, glad) as frown is to (smirk, sniff, scowl)

41) Everybody is to (assembly, all, sundry) as nobody is to (nun, vicar, none)

42) Hair is to (hare, comb, human) as feather is to (pen, duck, pillow)

43) Frog is to (toad, tadpole, pond) as wasp is to (nest, bee, hornet)

44) Fire is to (orange, flame, hot) as ice is to (snow, water, cold)

In these questions there are four words. Three of the words have been given a code. The codes are not written in the same order as the words and one code is missing.

SPIN   TALK   PINT   NEST

1467   6237   3146

45) Work out the code for SENT.   _____

46) Work out the code for TINIEST.   _____

47) What is the word for 37213?   _____

BONE   NOTE   PAST   PEAT

2164   8476   5124

48) Work out the code for BEAN.   _____

49) Work out the code for PENNANT.   _____

50) What is the word for 816761?   _____

Score [   ] **Percentage** [**%**]

Verbal Reasoning Test 8

In these questions, one letter can be moved from the first word to the second word making two new words. The order of the letters must not be changed and the new words must make sense. Write the two new words or mark the letter that moves on your answer sheet.

Example:

climb	lose	limb	close

1) beast   cute   _____   _____

2) voice   pint   _____   _____

3) learnt   evens   _____   _____

4) plant   bank   _____   _____

5) range   grid   _____   _____

6) slide   fight   _____   _____

In these questions, find **one** word from **each** group that makes one correctly spelt word when joined together. The word from the first group always comes first. Underline **both** words.

Example:

(<u>motor</u> gas electric)   (engine bus <u>cycle</u>)

7) (thin thick slim)   (bird tree nest)

8) (go in come)   (lives dies exist)

9) (butter cheese eggs)   (mug cup glass)

10) (swerve avoid missed)   (able table seat)

11) (front side back)   (shoot fire duck)

12) (journey visit trip)   (let rent hers)

In each question, find the missing number that will complete the question correctly.

Example:

$25 + 17 - 3 = 12 \times 3 + ?$ _____3_____

13) $9 \times 6 - 10 = 100 - 52 - ?$ _____

14) $16 \times 4 - 3 = 8 \times 7 + ?$ _____

15) $72 \div 9 \times 2 = 4 \times 2 \times ?$ _____

16) $36 + 39 = 3 \times 5 \times ?$ _____

17) $3 \times 14 + 18 = 50 \times 6 \div ?$ _____

18) $11 \times 11 - 26 = 13 \times 6 + ?$ _____

In these questions, the middle number in the last group is made up in the same way as the middle numbers in the first two groups. Find the missing number and write it in the brackets.

Example:

(5 [15] 10)   (8 [17] 9)   (10 [30] 20)

19) (4 [22] 7)   (8 [28] 6)   (7 [   ] 11)

20) (6 [21] 9)   (8 [30] 14)   (5 [   ] 21)

21) (25 [60] 33)   (45 [74] 27)   (38 [   ] 46)

22) (7 [39] 5)   (6 [52] 8)   (4 [   ] 9)

23) (36 [22] 7)   (45 [27] 9)   (48 [   ] 8)

24) (81 [11] 9)   (72 [8] 12)   (121 [   ] 11)

In these questions there are two pairs of words. One of the five answers will go equally well with both pairs of words. Find the word.

Example:

    (steady   firm)   (barn   shed)   *stable*

    office   chain   beach   farm   stable

25) (rush   hurry)   (energise   refill)   _____

    speed   refuel   race   quick   charge

26) (wave   flap)   (supporter   follower)   _____

    sea   point   enthuse   fan   direct

27) (tip   end)   (show   direct)   _____

    summit   point   produce   send   target

28) (difficult   awkward)   (firm   solid)   _____

    tough   hard   frozen   uneasy   sturdy

29) (level   smooth)   (home   apartment)   _____

    house   abode   flat   plane   bland

30) (edge   face)   (team   group)   _____

    squad   corner   vertice   side   fringe

Read the following information then find the correct answer.

31) Jan, Andy, Roy, Denise and Nick are all given house points by their teacher during the week.

Jan received three times as many as Denise, who received 3 less than Andy. Nick was given 2 more than Denise. Andy received two less than Roy, who received 8 points.

Which one of the following statements is true?   _____

A. Roy received the most house points during the week.
B. Andy received twice as many as Denise.
C. Nick received the least number of house points.
D. One child received more than 10 house points.
E. The children live in a bungalow and so don't get house points.

In these questions there are three pairs of words. The last pair of words is made up in the same way as the first two pairs. Find the missing word and write it in the brackets.

Example:

    (grind grin)   (fore for)   (piper [*pipe*])

32) (bread bad)   (plain pin)   (basin [   ])

33) (blade dale)   (anode done)   (spate [   ])

34) (target rate)   (volley love)   (matter [   ])

35) (client tile)   (cooker rook)   (feeder [   ])

36) (asleep pale)   (antler rate)   (issuer [   ])

37) (record core)   (demand made)   (design [   ])

Read the following information then find the correct answer.

38) Lisa, Zoe and Maxine bought some fizzy drinks from the supermarket for a party.

Lisa bought 3 large bottles and 1 medium bottle.
Zoe bought 5 medium bottles. Maxine bought 2 bottles of each.
Large bottles contain 3 litres. 2 large bottles contains the same amount as 3 medium bottles.

How many litres did the girls buy altogether?   _____ litres

A B C D E F G H I J K L M N O P Q R S T U V W X Y Z

The above alphabet is there to help you with these questions. Find the next letters in the sequence and write them in the brackets.

Example:

AB	BC	CD	DE	EF	(FG)

39)	KG	JK	HO	ES	AW	( )
40)	FD	IG	LJ	OM	RP	( )
41)	BK	CJ	EM	FL	HO	( )
42)	PX	NC	KY	GB	BZ	( )
43)	GG	HF	IE	JD	( )	
44)	BF	EG	ID	LE	PB	( )

In these questions there are four words. Three of the words have been given a code. The codes are not written in the same order as the words and one code is missing.

BARE   DATE   BEER   READ

3425   5264   7234

45) Work out the code for BREAD. _____

46) Work out the code for DARTED. _____

47) What is the word for 632545? _____

DOME   MILK   CALM   EARL

5396   1367   7468

48) Work out the code for CLAIM. _____

49) Work out the code for MARKER. _____

50) What is the word for 957385? _____

Score ☐ **Percentage** ☐ **%**

Verbal Reasoning Test 9

In these questions the **same** letter will fit into **both** sets of brackets, to end the word in front of the brackets and start the word after the brackets.

Example:

blas [t] reason   shor [t] rip

1)   stee [   ] ry   lea [   ] ried

2)   sla [   ] ink   clas [   ] ark

3)   spar [   ] ick   stor [   ] eeper

4)   trai [   ] ight   kil [   ] odge

5)   plan [   ] ing   slic [   ] eep

6)   cree [   ] air   tuli [   ] inch

In these questions, three of the five words are connected in some way. Find the **two** words that **do not** go with these three.

Example:

Monday Tuesday Friday midnight noon   ___midnight___ and ___noon___

7) carrot turnip cabbage bean potato   _____ and _____

8) compass north protractor east ruler   _____ and _____

9) chair bed sofa bunk bench   _____ and _____

10) circle oval square ellipse triangle   _____ and _____

11) defect flaw change error swap   _____ and _____

12) tell order request enquire ask   _____ and _____

In these questions, underline **two** words, one from each group, that are closest in meaning.

Example:

    (<u>sleep</u> run walk)   (smile laugh <u>snooze</u>)

13) (iron gold silver)   (press lead follow)

14) (clock watch chain)   (space telescope observe)

15) (petrol gas energy)   (speed power accelerate)

16) (change coin pound)   (note charge hit)

17) (silent noisy hiss)   (quite quit hushed)

18) (fall rise climb)   (clamp clamber mountain)

In each question, find the missing number that will complete the question correctly.

Example:

$$25 + 17 - 3 = 12 \times 3 + ?$$ <u> 3 </u>

19) $16 \times 3 + 9 = 46 + ?$ _____

20) $8 \times 3 + 3 = 17 + 18 - ?$ _____

21) $56 \div 8 \times 2 = 65 - 17 - ?$ _____

22) $8 \times 9 - 12 = 3 \times 4 \times ?$ _____

23) $122 - 39 - 11 = 45 + 27 + ?$ _____

24) $200 \div 4 + 12 = 9 \times 6 + ?$ _____

In these sentences, a four-letter word can be found at the end of one word and the beginning of the next word. Find the two words that contain the hidden word and write it on the line.

Example:

    The pro<u>be st</u>reaked through outer space.   *best*

25) Choir members visit church on Sunday mornings.   _____

26) Simon's piano teacher usually plays very well.   _____

27) Mother paid the old milkman yesterday.   _____

28) Many people live near that picturesque village.   _____

29) Soldiers never march inside their barracks.   _____

30) Some magic ointment healed the knight's wounds.   _____

Read the following information then find the correct answer.

31) Lauren, Mark and Jessica collect bean bag animals.

    Lauren has three times as many as Jessica.
    Mark has half as many as Jessica.
    They have 36 bean bag animals altogether.

    Which one of the following statements is true?   _____

    A. Jessica and Mark have 15 between them.
    B. Lauren has 10 more bean bag animals than Jessica.
    C. Lauren has 24 bean bag animals.
    D. Mark doesn't like bean bag animals.
    E. Jessica has only 6 bean bag animals.

A B C D E F G H I J K L M N O P Q R S T U V W X Y Z

The above alphabet is there to help you with these questions. Each question has a different code. Work out the second code or word as instructed.

Example:

The code for TRAP is USBQ.
What is the word for DPME?   <u> COLD </u>

32) The code for SCIENCE is UBKDPBG.
What is the word for DKCRVDF?   _____

33) The code for HOUSES is MTZXJX.
Work out the code for ESTATE.   _____

34) The code for AMAZE is ZOXDZ.
What is the word for OTFGZ?   _____

35) The code for SILENCE is XDQZSXJ.
Work out the code for QUIETLY.   _____

36) The code for FLEET is KPHGU.
What is the word for BEOGT?   _____

37) The code for MARKET is QEVOIX.
Work out the code for GROCER.   _____

A B C D E F G H I J K L M N O P Q R S T U V W X Y Z

The above alphabet is there to help you with these questions. Find the next letters in the sequence and write them in the brackets.

Example:

AB	BC	CD	DE	EF	(FG)

38) WC   AD   EF   II   MM   (   )

39) SJ   TG   RD   SA   QX   (   )

40) MR   MP   NN   NL   OJ   (   )

41) NT   TQ   ZN   FK   LH   (   )

42) WV   XX   ZZ   CB   GD   (   )

43) FK   GJ   EL   FK   DM   (   )

Read the following information then find the correct answer.

44) Jeremy, Mandy, Andrew, Michael and Joan buy sweets from the local sweet shop.

Mandy and Michael buy 6 chews each.
Jeremy and Joan buy 3 lollipops each.
Andrew and Michael each buy 2 chocolate bars.
Joan and Mandy buy 8 gobstoppers between them.
Jeremy and Andrew buy 8 liquorice laces each.

Who buys the most items?   _____

In these questions, the word in the middle of the second group is made in the **same way** as the word in the middle of the first group. Find the word that is missing in the second group.

Example:

(lint   [liner]   term)

(drop   [   ]   even)   _____drove_____

45) (blame   [dream]   trade)

(plank   [   ]   slice)   _____

46) (freed   [fresh]   shore)

(today   [   ]   chief)   _____

47) (claim   [small]   snail)

(angel   [   ]   build)   _____

48) (zebra   [bears]   horse)

(lunar   [   ]   laser)   _____

49) (diets   [tried]   older)

(march   [   ]   pupil)   _____

50) (chair   [reach]   share)

(stiff   [   ]   knave)   _____

Score [   ] Percentage [   ] %

Verbal Reasoning Test 10

In these questions, one letter can be moved from the first word to the second word making two new words. The order of the letters must not be changed and the new words must make sense. Write the two new words or mark the letter that moves on your answer sheet.

Example:

			limb	close
	climb	lose	_limb_	_close_
1)	cheap	shin	_____	_____
2)	solid	bran	_____	_____
3)	waiter	clam	_____	_____
4)	plane	sell	_____	_____
5)	braked	bead	_____	_____
6)	places	sides	_____	_____

In these sentences, the word in capitals has had **three** letters next to each other taken out. Find the word that is made from these letters without changing their order. The sentence that you make must make sense.

Example:

John bought a new COMER.	COM**PUT**ER	_PUT_
7) I saw my friend SDING on the corner.		_____
8) The police officer showed great CAGE arresting the thief.		_____
9) Elizabeth always writes NLY in her book.		_____
10) The mechanic worked all day in the GAE.		_____
11) Jane spent 50p on a packet of coloured CONS.		_____
12) Simon WERED along in a world of his own.		_____

In these questions, underline **two** words, one from each group, that have the most opposite meaning.

Example:

    (<u>up</u> run walk)   (smile laugh <u>down</u>)

13) (start finish waste)   (condemn commend commence)

14) (exchange sell buy)   (pursuit perfume purchase)

15) (wheel lend tunnel)   (burrow borrow barrow)

16) (defeat defend deflate)   (lose victory winner)

17) (contact agreed contract)   (touch smash expand)

18) (yell shout loud)   (hard soft talk)

In these questions, find one word from each pair of brackets that will complete the sentence in the best way. Underline **both** words.

Example:

    Time is to (first, <u>second,</u> third) as distance is to (gram, kilo, <u>metre</u>)

19) Say is to (mention, tell, said) as find is to (determine, found, discover)

20) Rugby is to (shot, kick, try) as football is to (goal, penalty, save)

21) Coffee is to (drink, bean, cup) as tea is to (leaf, bag, golf)

22) Century is to (thousand, hundred, million) as decade is to (ten, twenty, fifty)

23) Key is to (lock, door, quay) as weight is to (heavy, wait, kilo)

24) Light is to (bulb, sun, heavy) as dull is to (brilliant, excellent, superb)

In each question, find the next number in the sequence and write it in the brackets.

Example:

    5   10   15   20   25 (30)

25) 8   15   12   19   16 (   )

26) 121 81 49 25 (   )

27) 13 16 20 25 31 (   )

28) 22 21 23 23 24 25 25 (   )

29) 23 25 20 22 18 20 17 (   )

30) 93 92 95 95 97 98 (   )

Read the following information then find the correct answer.

31) Rodney, Albert, Cassie, Raquel and Derek weigh themselves in a science experiment at school.

    Derek weighs more than Raquel, but less than Albert. Rodney weighs more than Cassie, but is lighter than Derek.

    Who is the heaviest?   _____

A B C D E F G H I J K L M N O P Q R S T U V W X Y Z

The above alphabet is there to help you with these questions. Find the letters that complete each question in the best way.

Example:

    DE is to FG as ST is to (UV)

32) PO is to LA as ML is to (   )

33) EA is to CX as AC is to (   )

34) ML is to NO as PQ is to (   )

35) GM is to DQ as JI is to (   )

36) YA is to BX as XZ is to (   )

37) LL is to OH as TS is to (   )

In these questions, find **one** word from **each** group that makes one correctly spelt word when joined together. The word from the first group always comes first. Underline **both** words.

Example:

(<u>motor</u> gas electric)   (engine bus <u>cycle</u>)

38) (fly bug ant)   (them hem they)

39) (on off in)   (leap jump spring)

40) (feat deed dare)   (ring her full)

41) (proper tidy prim)   (fed ate eat)

42) (circle ring round)   (ruler leader chief)

43) (six ate ten)   (ant bug fly)

In these questions letters stand for numbers. Work out the answer to the sum, find its letter and write it in the brackets.

Example:

If $A = 2$, $B = 3$, $C = 4$, $D = 5$ and $E = 1$,

what is the answer to this sum, **written as a letter**?

$A + B - E = [\ C\ ]$

44) If $A = 6$, $B = 12$, $C = 8$, $D = 3$ and $E = 9$,

what is the answer to this sum, **written as a letter**?

$B \div D + C - A = [\ \ ]$

45) If $A = 2$, $B = 24$, $C = 30$, $D = 9$ and $E = 18$,

what is the answer to this sum, **written as a letter**?

$A \times E + B - C = [\ \ ]$

46) If $A = 0$, $B = 2$, $C = 4$, $D = 8$ and $E = 10$,

what is the answer to this sum, **written as a letter**?

$D \div B \times E \times A = [\ \ ]$

47) If **A = 20, B = 10, C = 4, D = 5** and **E = 2**,
what is the answer to this sum, **written as a letter**?

$A \times B \div C \div D = [\quad]$

48) If **A = 6, B = 8, C = 17, D = 25** and **E = 11**,
what is the answer to this sum, **written as a letter**?

$D - E - B + C - A = [\quad]$

49) If **A = 2, B = 9, C = 16, D = 12** and **E = 3**,
what is the answer to this sum, **written as a letter**?

$D - B + C - E = [\quad]$

Read the following information then find the correct answer.

50) Geoffrey, Joseph, Nick, Susan and Margaret play musical instruments in the school orchestra. They practise very hard.

Susan and Geoffrey practise for 4 hours on Monday.
Nick, Joseph and Margaret practise for 2 hours on Tuesday.
Geoffrey, Nick and Margaret practise for 2 hours on Wednesday.
Joseph and Geoffrey practise for 2 hours on Thursday.
Margaret and Susan practise for 3 hours on Friday.
Nick and Susan practise for 3 hours on Saturday.

Which person practises for the most hours during the week? _____

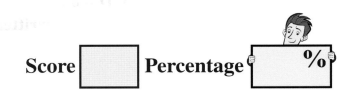

Score [   ] Percentage [   ] %

Multiple-choice Answer Sheet
Verbal Reasoning Year 5-7 GL & Other Styles Testbook 6: Test 1

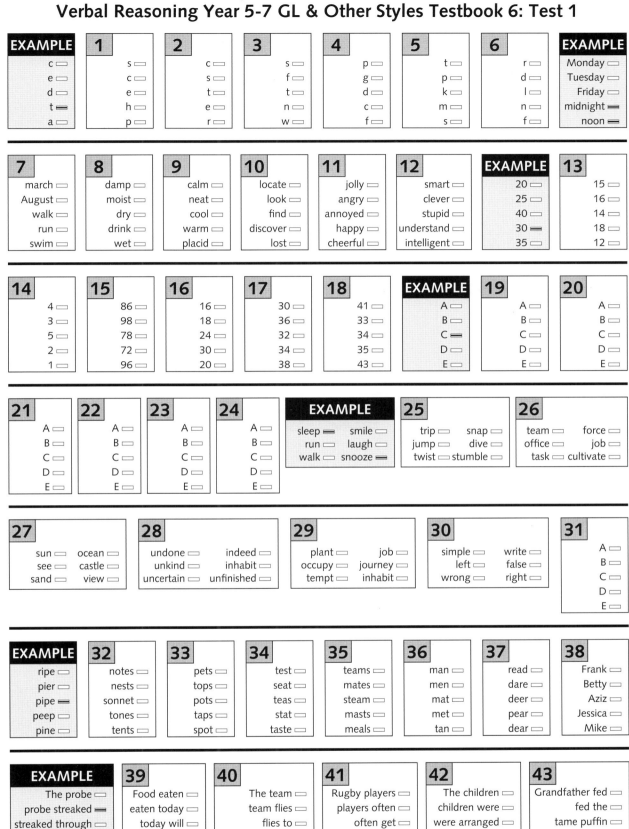

Multiple-choice Answer Sheet
Verbal Reasoning Year 5-7 GL & Other Styles Testbook 6: Test 2

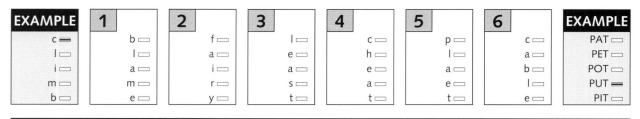

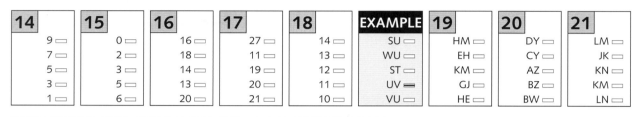

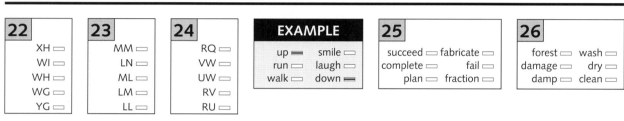

© 2016 Stephen Curran

Multiple-choice Answer Sheet
Verbal Reasoning Year 5-7 GL & Other Styles Testbook 6: Test 3

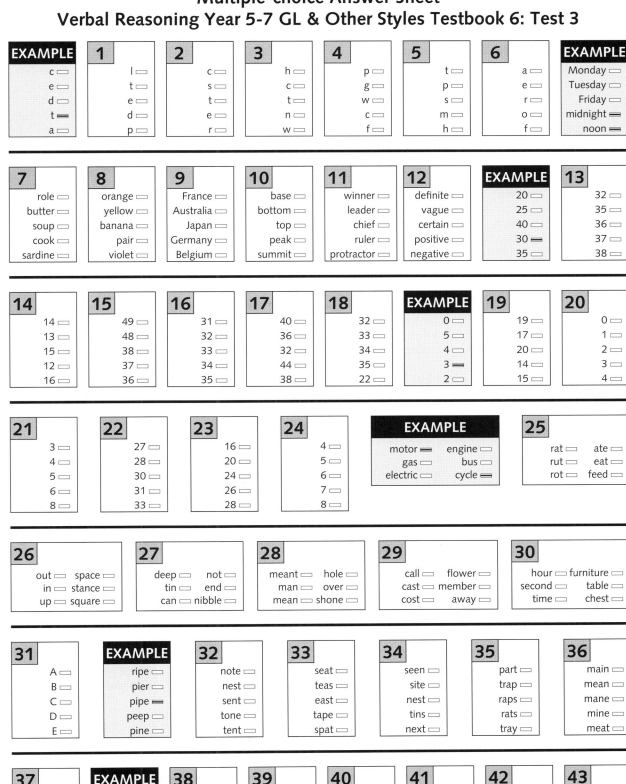

EXAMPLE
- c
- e
- d
- t ▪
- a

1
- l
- t
- e
- d
- p

2
- c
- s
- t
- e
- r

3
- h
- c
- t
- n
- w

4
- p
- g
- w
- c
- f

5
- t
- p
- s
- m
- h

6
- a
- e
- r
- o
- f

EXAMPLE
- Monday
- Tuesday
- Friday
- midnight ▪
- noon ▪

7
- role
- butter
- soup
- cook
- sardine

8
- orange
- yellow
- banana
- pair
- violet

9
- France
- Australia
- Japan
- Germany
- Belgium

10
- base
- bottom
- top
- peak
- summit

11
- winner
- leader
- chief
- ruler
- protractor

12
- definite
- vague
- certain
- positive
- negative

EXAMPLE
- 20
- 25
- 40
- 30 ▪
- 35

13
- 32
- 35
- 36
- 37
- 38

14
- 14
- 13
- 15
- 12
- 16

15
- 49
- 48
- 38
- 37
- 36

16
- 31
- 32
- 33
- 34
- 35

17
- 40
- 36
- 32
- 44
- 38

18
- 32
- 33
- 34
- 35
- 22

EXAMPLE
- 0
- 5
- 4
- 3 ▪
- 2

19
- 19
- 17
- 20
- 14
- 15

20
- 0
- 1
- 2
- 3
- 4

21
- 3
- 4
- 5
- 6
- 8

22
- 27
- 28
- 30
- 31
- 33

23
- 16
- 20
- 24
- 26
- 28

24
- 4
- 5
- 6
- 7
- 8

EXAMPLE
- motor ▪
- gas
- electric
- engine
- bus
- cycle ▪

25
- rat
- rut
- rot
- ate
- eat
- feed

26
- out
- in
- up
- space
- stance
- square

27
- deep
- tin
- can
- not
- end
- nibble

28
- meant
- man
- mean
- hole
- over
- shone

29
- call
- cast
- cost
- flower
- member
- away

30
- hour
- second
- time
- furniture
- table
- chest

31
- A
- B
- C
- D
- E

EXAMPLE
- ripe
- pier
- pipe ▪
- peep
- pine

32
- note
- nest
- sent
- tone
- tent

33
- seat
- teas
- east
- tape
- spat

34
- seen
- site
- nest
- tins
- next

35
- part
- trap
- raps
- rats
- tray

36
- main
- mean
- mane
- mine
- meat

37
- near
- real
- race
- lean
- lace

EXAMPLE
- GH
- EG
- EF
- FG ▪
- GF

38
- TV
- SV
- ST
- TU
- SU

39
- WX
- XY
- WZ
- YZ
- ZA

40
- CI
- DF
- IF
- ID
- IC

41
- WX
- WZ
- YZ
- YY
- YX

42
- OP
- NP
- PN
- PO
- PQ

43
- UU
- RU
- WX
- VT
- TV

44
- Peter
- Mary
- Julie
- Harriet
- James

EXAMPLE
- office
- chain
- beach
- farm
- stable ▪

45
- blast
- inferno
- fire
- submerge
- liftoff

46
- wings
- duck
- chicken
- bend
- sit

47
- fall
- bath
- sink
- lose
- throw

48
- cash
- loot
- smash
- crash
- pound

49
- true
- write
- change
- correct
- return

50
- colour
- write
- same
- draw
- paint

Multiple-choice Answer Sheet
Verbal Reasoning Year 5-7 GL & Other Styles Testbook 6: Test 4

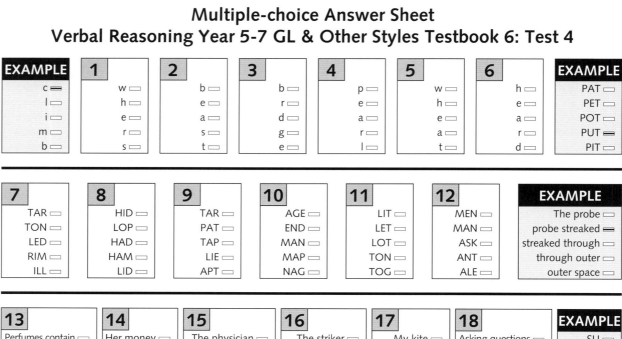

EXAMPLE
- c ▬
- l ▢
- i ▢
- m ▢
- b ▢

1
- w ▢
- h ▢
- e ▢
- r ▢
- s ▢

2
- b ▢
- e ▢
- s ▢
- t ▢

3
- b ▢
- r ▢
- d ▢
- g ▢
- e ▢

4
- p ▢
- e ▢
- a ▢
- r ▢
- l ▢

5
- w ▢
- h ▢
- e ▢
- t ▢

6
- h ▢
- e ▢
- a ▢
- r ▢
- d ▢

EXAMPLE
- PAT ▢
- PET ▢
- POT ▢
- PUT ▬
- PIT ▢

7
- TAR ▢
- TON ▢
- LED ▢
- RIM ▢
- ILL ▢

8
- HID ▢
- LOP ▢
- HAD ▢
- HAM ▢
- LID ▢

9
- TAR ▢
- PAT ▢
- TAP ▢
- LIE ▢
- APT ▢

10
- AGE ▢
- END ▢
- MAN ▢
- MAP ▢
- NAG ▢

11
- LIT ▢
- LET ▢
- LOT ▢
- TON ▢
- TOG ▢

12
- MEN ▢
- MAN ▢
- ASK ▢
- ANT ▢
- ALE ▢

EXAMPLE
- The probe ▢
- probe streaked ▬
- streaked through ▢
- through outer ▢
- outer space ▢

13
- Perfumes contain ▢
- contain ice ▢
- ice water ▢
- water from ▢
- mountain springs ▢

14
- Her money ▢
- money fell ▢
- fell from ▢
- her open ▢
- open purse ▢

15
- The physician ▢
- physician treated ▢
- treated her ▢
- her patient's ▢
- patient's illnesses ▢

16
- The striker ▢
- striker spun ▢
- spun towards ▢
- towards the ▢
- the goal ▢

17
- My kite ▢
- kite might ▢
- might blow ▢
- blow away ▢
- away today ▢

18
- Asking questions ▢
- questions will ▢
- will improve ▢
- improve your ▢
- your knowledge ▢

EXAMPLE
- SU ▢
- WU ▢
- ST ▢
- UV ▬
- VU ▢

19
- HM ▢
- EH ▢
- QL ▢
- QS ▢
- HE ▢

20
- KH ▢
- JC ▢
- JG ▢
- KL ▢
- HL ▢

21
- LO ▢
- OK ▢
- KN ▢
- KM ▢
- ON ▢

22
- FR ▢
- FS ▢
- FT ▢
- DT ▢
- EV ▢

23
- OQ ▢
- OS ▢
- OT ▢
- OP ▢
- OR ▢

24
- TV ▢
- TW ▢
- UW ▢
- ST ▢
- RV ▢

EXAMPLE
- 25 ▢
- 15 ▢
- 24 ▢
- 30 ▬
- 10 ▢

25
- 18 ▢
- 30 ▢
- 28 ▢
- 34 ▢
- 24 ▢

26
- 16 ▢
- 18 ▢
- 19 ▢
- 20 ▢
- 9 ▢

27
- 22 ▢
- 21 ▢
- 25 ▢
- 26 ▢
- 23 ▢

28
- 37 ▢
- 39 ▢
- 38 ▢
- 35 ▢
- 36 ▢

29
- 130 ▢
- 126 ▢
- 118 ▢
- 124 ▢
- 102 ▢

30
- 98 ▢
- 101 ▢
- 108 ▢
- 103 ▢
- 106 ▢

EXAMPLE
- COLT ▢
- CLAN ▢
- CAST ▢
- COAL ▢
- COLD ▬

31
- REALM ▢
- PLATE ▢
- PLANE ▢
- RAVEN ▢
- PLANK ▢

32
- CLEKUJK ▢
- GPINJJU ▢
- GOINLVK ▢
- CLINUJK ▢
- GPINKUJ ▢

33
- WORMS ▢
- WORST ▢
- WARTS ▢
- WORRY ▢
- WORSE ▢

34
- ORACLE ▢
- ORPHAN ▢
- ORCHID ▢
- ORANGE ▢
- ORDERS ▢

35
- FIELD ▢
- FIXED ▢
- FIXES ▢
- FIRST ▢
- FIVER ▢

36
- FINE ▢
- HOST ▢
- FATE ▢
- HATE ▢
- FACE ▢

37
- Michelle ▢
- Sheila ▢
- John ▢
- Jenny ▢
- Freda ▢

38
- A ▢
- B ▢
- C ▢
- D ▢
- E ▢

EXAMPLE
- A ▢
- B ▢
- C ▬
- D ▢
- E ▢

39
- A ▢
- B ▢
- C ▢
- D ▢
- E ▢

40
- A ▢
- B ▢
- C ▢
- D ▢
- E ▢

41
- A ▢
- B ▢
- C ▢
- D ▢
- E ▢

42
- A ▢
- B ▢
- C ▢
- D ▢
- E ▢

43
- A ▢
- B ▢
- C ▢
- D ▢
- E ▢

44
- A ▢
- B ▢
- C ▢
- D ▢
- E ▢

EXAMPLE
- sleep ▬
- run ▢
- walk ▢
- smile ▢
- laugh ▢
- snooze ▬

45
- hole ▢
- part ▢
- fraction ▢
- whole ▢
- roll ▢
- role ▢

46
- tree ▢
- banana ▢
- tear ▢
- leave ▢
- split ▢
- depart ▢

47
- deceitful ▢
- disconnect ▢
- delegate ▢
- dislike ▢
- distrust ▢
- dishonest ▢

48
- article ▢
- appoint ▢
- argue ▢
- retire ▢
- disagree ▢
- discharge ▢

49
- strand ▢
- pine ▢
- pullover ▢
- needle ▢
- thread ▢
- knit ▢

50
- darkness ▢
- pair ▢
- match ▢
- flame ▢
- contest ▢
- light ▢

Multiple-choice Answer Sheet
Verbal Reasoning Year 5-7 GL & Other Styles Testbook 6: Test 5

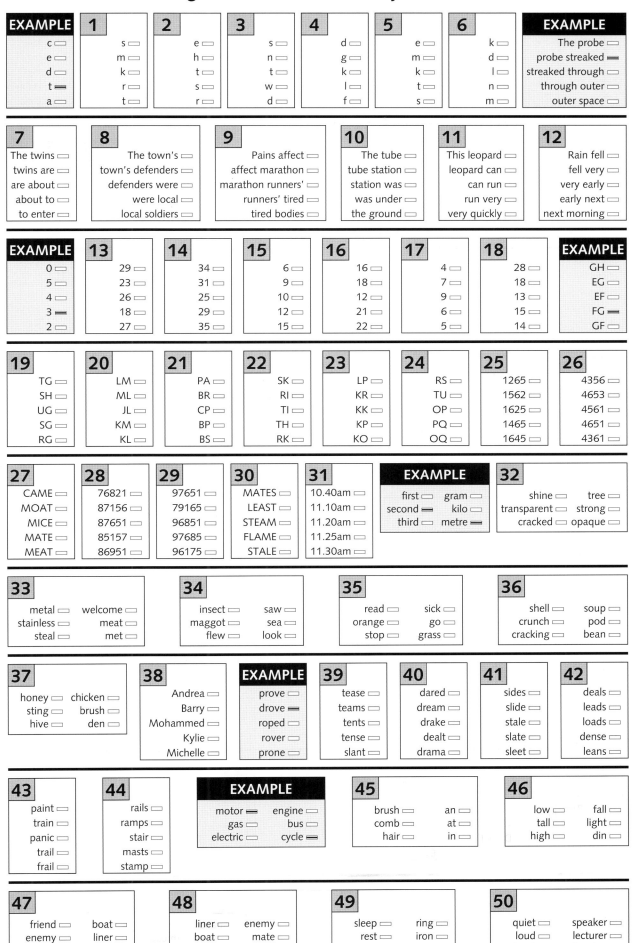

© 2016 Stephen Curran

Multiple-choice Answer Sheet
Verbal Reasoning Year 5-7 GL & Other Styles Testbook 6: Test 6

EXAMPLE
- c ▆
- l ▢
- i ▢
- m ▢
- b ▢

1
- s ▢
- t ▢
- o ▢
- c ▢
- k ▢

2
- s ▢
- t ▢
- e ▢
- a ▢
- m ▢

3
- r ▢
- a ▢
- n ▢
- g ▢
- e ▢

4
- c ▢
- r ▢
- a ▢
- t ▢
- e ▢

5
- n ▢
- a ▢
- t ▢
- i ▢
- v ▢

6
- c ▢
- r ▢
- a ▢
- k ▢
- m ▢

EXAMPLE
- Monday ▢
- Tuesday ▢
- Friday ▢
- midnight ▆
- noon ▢

7
- smack ▢
- bounce ▢
- hit ▢
- spring ▢
- strike ▢

8
- cut ▢
- slim ▢
- trim ▢
- chop ▢
- fat ▢

9
- first ▢
- aid ▢
- assist ▢
- medicine ▢
- help ▢

10
- irregular ▢
- abnormal ▢
- usual ▢
- unusual ▢
- normal ▢

11
- imitate ▢
- copy ▢
- write ▢
- draw ▢
- mimic ▢

12
- money ▢
- forgery ▢
- fake ▢
- copy ▢
- appear ▢

EXAMPLE
- 20 ▢
- 25 ▢
- 40 ▢
- 30 ▆
- 35 ▢

13
- 24 ▢
- 29 ▢
- 25 ▢
- 30 ▢
- 28 ▢

14
- 14 ▢
- 13 ▢
- 15 ▢
- 12 ▢
- 11 ▢

15
- 200 ▢
- 210 ▢
- 220 ▢
- 240 ▢
- 260 ▢

16
- 12 ▢
- 13 ▢
- 24 ▢
- 21 ▢
- 23 ▢

17
- 11 ▢
- 14 ▢
- 15 ▢
- 13 ▢
- 12 ▢

18
- 41 ▢
- 33 ▢
- 34 ▢
- 35 ▢
- 43 ▢

EXAMPLE
- 0 ▢
- 5 ▢
- 4 ▢
- 3 ▆
- 2 ▢

19
- 28 ▢
- 31 ▢
- 29 ▢
- 30 ▢
- 35 ▢

20
- 20 ▢
- 26 ▢
- 27 ▢
- 25 ▢
- 23 ▢

21
- 3 ▢
- 5 ▢
- 4 ▢
- 6 ▢
- 7 ▢

22
- 9 ▢
- 13 ▢
- 10 ▢
- 15 ▢
- 20 ▢

23
- 5 ▢
- 15 ▢
- 12 ▢
- 20 ▢
- 10 ▢

24
- 2 ▢
- 5 ▢
- 4 ▢
- 3 ▢
- 7 ▢

EXAMPLE
- SU ▢
- WU ▢
- ST ▢
- UV ▆
- VU ▢

25
- GV ▢
- HV ▢
- HT ▢
- HS ▢
- HX ▢

26
- PY ▢
- YP ▢
- EH ▢
- JF ▢
- PW ▢

27
- JR ▢
- JS ▢
- IS ▢
- IQ ▢
- JQ ▢

28
- HJ ▢
- IG ▢
- IJ ▢
- HI ▢
- HK ▢

29
- GS ▢
- GT ▢
- GM ▢
- GR ▢
- HS ▢

30
- WX ▢
- WZ ▢
- ZY ▢
- ZW ▢
- WY ▢

31
- A ▢
- B ▢
- C ▢
- D ▢
- E ▢

EXAMPLE
- ripe ▢
- pier ▢
- pipe ▆
- peep ▢
- pine ▢

32
- lame ▢
- male ▢
- leaf ▢
- meal ▢
- flea ▢

33
- test ▢
- pest ▢
- west ▢
- nest ▢
- rest ▢

34
- free ▢
- roof ▢
- fore ▢
- rose ▢
- reef ▢

35
- males ▢
- realm ▢
- mares ▢
- meals ▢
- blame ▢

36
- rake ▢
- bear ▢
- bare ▢
- cake ▢
- care ▢

37
- trap ▢
- part ▢
- port ▢
- rota ▢
- roar ▢

38
- Saeeda ▢
- Harry ▢
- Nick ▢
- Katie ▢
- Michelle ▢

EXAMPLE
- sleep ▆
- run ▢
- walk ▢
- smile ▢
- laugh ▢
- snooze ▆

39
- spotted ▢
- striped ▢
- coloured ▢
- blank ▢
- seen ▢
- scene ▢

40
- jump ▢
- walk ▢
- trot ▢
- leap ▢
- spin ▢
- swim ▢

41
- complete ▢
- complicate ▢
- complain ▢
- ending ▢
- beginning ▢
- finish ▢

42
- soap ▢
- laundry ▢
- brush ▢
- washing ▢
- powder ▢
- liquid ▢

43
- crook ▢
- crop ▢
- crock ▢
- shepherd ▢
- rustler ▢
- criminal ▢

44
- cube ▢
- bucket ▢
- box ▢
- spade ▢
- sugar ▢
- fight ▢

EXAMPLE
- prove ▢
- drove ▆
- roped ▢
- rover ▢
- prone ▢

45
- deals ▢
- dates ▢
- dents ▢
- dales ▢
- dense ▢

46
- grain ▢
- trail ▢
- trial ▢
- grant ▢
- train ▢

47
- great ▢
- cried ▢
- grate ▢
- dried ▢
- creed ▢

48
- drive ▢
- drove ▢
- drill ▢
- drops ▢
- dried ▢

49
- biker ▢
- train ▢
- write ▢
- wreck ▢
- brain ▢

50
- nasal ▢
- India ▢
- naval ▢
- nails ▢
- snail ▢

Multiple-choice Answer Sheet
Verbal Reasoning Year 5-7 GL & Other Styles Testbook 6: Test 7

EXAMPLE
- up ▬
- smile ▢
- run ▢
- laugh ▢
- walk ▢
- down ▬

1
- inside ▢
- surface ▢
- superior ▢
- exterior ▢
- volume ▢
- interior ▢

2
- dear ▢
- cheep ▢
- deer ▢
- cheap ▢
- mouse ▢
- cat ▢

3
- solid ▢
- difficult ▢
- hard ▢
- smooth ▢
- rough ▢
- shiny ▢

4
- backward ▢
- inwards ▢
- upwards ▢
- outward ▢
- downward ▢
- forward ▢

5
- wild ▢
- angry ▢
- dense ▢
- garden ▢
- overgrown ▢
- calm ▢

6
- push ▢
- open ▢
- clamp ▢
- close ▢
- shut ▢
- slam ▢

EXAMPLE
- PAT ▢
- PET ▢
- POT ▢
- PUT ▬
- PIT ▢

7
- CON ▢
- CAN ▢
- TIN ▢
- VET ▢
- BIN ▢

8
- OUR ▢
- ARE ▢
- ALL ▢
- AND ▢
- OLD ▢

9
- EGG ▢
- END ▢
- ASH ▢
- ASK ▢
- ASS ▢

10
- VAT ▢
- HAT ▢
- MAT ▢
- VET ▢
- GET ▢

11
- ANY ▢
- AND ▢
- INK ▢
- IMP ▢
- ALE ▢

12
- EWE ▢
- OIL ▢
- EVE ▢
- END ▢
- OUT ▢

EXAMPLE
- c ▢
- e ▢
- d ▢
- t ▬
- a ▢

13
- b ▢
- d ▢
- w ▢
- g ▢
- n ▢

14
- k ▢
- e ▢
- t ▢
- r ▢
- y ▢

15
- n ▢
- f ▢
- r ▢
- s ▢
- l ▢

16
- p ▢
- c ▢
- s ▢
- w ▢
- b ▢

17
- f ▢
- e ▢
- d ▢
- r ▢
- t ▢

18
- y ▢
- c ▢
- t ▢
- b ▢
- d ▢

EXAMPLE
- A ▢
- B ▢
- C ▬
- D ▢
- E ▢

19
- A ▢
- B ▢
- C ▢
- D ▢
- E ▢

20
- A ▢
- B ▢
- C ▢
- D ▢
- E ▢

21
- A ▢
- B ▢
- C ▢
- D ▢
- E ▢

22
- A ▢
- B ▢
- C ▢
- D ▢
- E ▢

23
- A ▢
- B ▢
- C ▢
- D ▢
- E ▢

24
- A ▢
- B ▢
- C ▢
- D ▢
- E ▢

EXAMPLE
- 20 ▢
- 25 ▢
- 40 ▢
- 30 ▬
- 35 ▢

25
- 11 ▢
- 13 ▢
- 16 ▢
- 15 ▢
- 18 ▢

26
- 12 ▢
- 17 ▢
- 15 ▢
- 13 ▢
- 14 ▢

27
- 50 ▢
- 96 ▢
- 52 ▢
- 60 ▢
- 72 ▢

28
- 16 ▢
- 11 ▢
- 14 ▢
- 13 ▢
- 12 ▢

29
- 27 ▢
- 28 ▢
- 33 ▢
- 30 ▢
- 31 ▢

30
- 14 ▢
- 13 ▢
- 12 ▢
- 11 ▢
- 10 ▢

EXAMPLE
- COLT ▢
- CLAN ▢
- CAST ▢
- COAL ▢
- COLD ▬

31
- MINUET ▢
- MINUTE ▢
- MINCER ▢
- MANTEL ▢
- MISTER ▢

32
- VTXLNTN ▢
- USKLNTK ▢
- XSKLXTN ▢
- USKXNLN ▢
- XTLXNTN ▢

33
- BLIND ▢
- BLEAK ▢
- BLAME ▢
- BREAK ▢
- BLOND ▢

34
- TSFRBNU ▢
- TGSXBPU ▢
- TUHTDPW ▢
- TGSXBNU ▢
- UGHTBNU ▢

35
- SLOPE ▢
- SLEEK ▢
- SLEET ▢
- SLEEP ▢
- SNOOP ▢

36
- FDOXCZI ▢
- FDPYDAJ ▢
- EDNWBAJ ▢
- EDNWAZI ▢
- EDNXCZI ▢

37
- 0 ▢
- 1 ▢
- 2 ▢
- 3 ▢
- 4 ▢

38
- A ▢
- B ▢
- C ▢
- D ▢
- E ▢

EXAMPLE
- first ▢
- gram ▢
- second ▬
- kilo ▢
- third ▢
- metre ▬

39
- hard ▢
- polluted ▢
- rotten ▢
- washed ▢
- fresh ▢
- filtered ▢

40
- happy ▢
- smirk ▢
- grin ▢
- sniff ▢
- glad ▢
- scowl ▢

41
- assembly ▢
- nun ▢
- all ▢
- vicar ▢
- sundry ▢
- none ▢

42
- hare ▢
- pen ▢
- comb ▢
- duck ▢
- human ▢
- pillow ▢

43
- toad ▢
- nest ▢
- tadpole ▢
- bee ▢
- pond ▢
- hornet ▢

44
- orange ▢
- snow ▢
- flame ▢
- water ▢
- hot ▢
- cold ▢

45
- 3267 ▢
- 3762 ▢
- 3276 ▢
- 7623 ▢
- 7632 ▢

46
- 7462437 ▢
- 7463427 ▢
- 7462347 ▢
- 7464237 ▢
- 7463472 ▢

47
- PESTS ▢
- SPINE ▢
- STONE ▢
- STEPS ▢
- SPENT ▢

48
- 5427 ▢
- 5472 ▢
- 5724 ▢
- 5742 ▢
- 5247 ▢

49
- 8477276 ▢
- 8422726 ▢
- 8724476 ▢
- 8747726 ▢
- 8622724 ▢

50
- POTATO ▢
- PATENT ▢
- BEATEN ▢
- BANTAM ▢
- POTION ▢

Multiple-choice Answer Sheet
Verbal Reasoning Year 5-7 GL & Other Styles Testbook 6: Test 8

EXAMPLE
- c ▬
- l ☐
- i ☐
- m ☐
- b ☐

1
- b ☐
- e ☐
- a ☐
- s ☐
- t ☐

2
- v ☐
- o ☐
- i ☐
- c ☐
- e ☐

3
- l ☐
- a ☐
- r ☐
- n ☐
- t ☐

4
- p ☐
- l ☐
- a ☐
- n ☐
- t ☐

5
- r ☐
- a ☐
- n ☐
- g ☐
- e ☐

6
- s ☐
- l ☐
- i ☐
- d ☐
- e ☐

EXAMPLE
- motor ▬   engine ☐
- gas ☐   bus ☐
- electric ☐   cycle ▬

7
- thin ☐   bird ☐
- thick ☐   tree ☐
- slim ☐   nest ☐

8
- go ☐   lives ☐
- in ☐   dies ☐
- come ☐   exist ☐

9
- butter ☐   mug ☐
- cheese ☐   cup ☐
- eggs ☐   glass ☐

10
- swerve ☐   able ☐
- avoid ☐   table ☐
- missed ☐   seat ☐

11
- front ☐   shoot ☐
- side ☐   fire ☐
- back ☐   duck ☐

12
- journey ☐   let ☐
- visit ☐   rent ☐
- trip ☐   hers ☐

EXAMPLE
- 0 ☐
- 5 ☐
- 4 ☐
- 3 ▬
- 2 ☐

13
- 4 ☐
- 3 ☐
- 6 ☐
- 8 ☐
- 7 ☐

14
- 4 ☐
- 1 ☐
- 5 ☐
- 9 ☐
- 3 ☐

15
- 0 ☐
- 1 ☐
- 4 ☐
- 2 ☐
- 3 ☐

16
- 7 ☐
- 8 ☐
- 2 ☐
- 6 ☐
- 5 ☐

17
- 4 ☐
- 7 ☐
- 9 ☐
- 6 ☐
- 5 ☐

18
- 17 ☐
- 18 ☐
- 13 ☐
- 15 ☐
- 14 ☐

EXAMPLE
- 25 ☐
- 15 ☐
- 24 ☐
- 30 ▬
- 10 ☐

19
- 38 ☐
- 44 ☐
- 28 ☐
- 34 ☐
- 36 ☐

20
- 26 ☐
- 31 ☐
- 29 ☐
- 30 ☐
- 27 ☐

21
- 82 ☐
- 81 ☐
- 88 ☐
- 86 ☐
- 78 ☐

22
- 38 ☐
- 42 ☐
- 40 ☐
- 35 ☐
- 37 ☐

23
- 32 ☐
- 40 ☐
- 42 ☐
- 36 ☐
- 38 ☐

24
- 9 ☐
- 11 ☐
- 13 ☐
- 10 ☐
- 12 ☐

EXAMPLE
- office ☐
- chain ☐
- beach ☐
- farm ☐
- stable ▬

25
- speed ☐
- refuel ☐
- race ☐
- quick ☐
- charge ☐

26
- sea ☐
- point ☐
- enthuse ☐
- fan ☐
- direct ☐

27
- summit ☐
- point ☐
- produce ☐
- send ☐
- target ☐

28
- tough ☐
- hard ☐
- frozen ☐
- uneasy ☐
- sturdy ☐

29
- house ☐
- abode ☐
- flat ☐
- plane ☐
- bland ☐

30
- squad ☐
- corner ☐
- vertice ☐
- side ☐
- fringe ☐

31
- A ☐
- B ☐
- C ☐
- D ☐
- E ☐

EXAMPLE
- ripe ☐
- pier ☐
- pipe ▬
- peep ☐
- pine ☐

32
- sin ☐
- ban ☐
- nab ☐
- bit ☐
- bin ☐

33
- peat ☐
- pest ☐
- tape ☐
- teas ☐
- taps ☐

34
- mare ☐
- tame ☐
- team ☐
- meat ☐
- tram ☐

35
- deer ☐
- reed ☐
- free ☐
- dear ☐
- dare ☐

36
- rise ☐
- sire ☐
- sure ☐
- site ☐
- sued ☐

37
- sing ☐
- send ☐
- dine ☐
- dice ☐
- side ☐

38
- 28 ☐
- 31 ☐
- 23 ☐
- 24 ☐
- 26 ☐

EXAMPLE
- GH ☐
- EG ☐
- EF ☐
- FG ▬
- GF ☐

39
- VA ☐
- VC ☐
- UC ☐
- XC ☐
- UA ☐

40
- TT ☐
- SS ☐
- UT ☐
- ST ☐
- US ☐

41
- HN ☐
- HO ☐
- IO ☐
- IP ☐
- IN ☐

42
- UA ☐
- VC ☐
- XC ☐
- UX ☐
- VA ☐

43
- LC ☐
- KC ☐
- LB ☐
- LD ☐
- KD ☐

44
- TD ☐
- RD ☐
- SC ☐
- RB ☐
- RE ☐

45
- 73524 ☐
- 73541 ☐
- 73425 ☐
- 73245 ☐
- 73452 ☐

46
- 523645 ☐
- 532645 ☐
- 532465 ☐
- 532564 ☐
- 532456 ☐

47
- BARTER ☐
- TRADER ☐
- BARRED ☐
- TRADED ☐
- TREADS ☐

48
- 16473 ☐
- 16437 ☐
- 16734 ☐
- 16537 ☐
- 16347 ☐

49
- 793853 ☐
- 739859 ☐
- 798538 ☐
- 739589 ☐
- 738958 ☐

50
- MILLER ☐
- CALLER ☐
- REMAKE ☐
- MAILER ☐
- KILLER ☐

Multiple-choice Answer Sheet
Verbal Reasoning Year 5-7 GL & Other Styles Testbook 6: Test 9

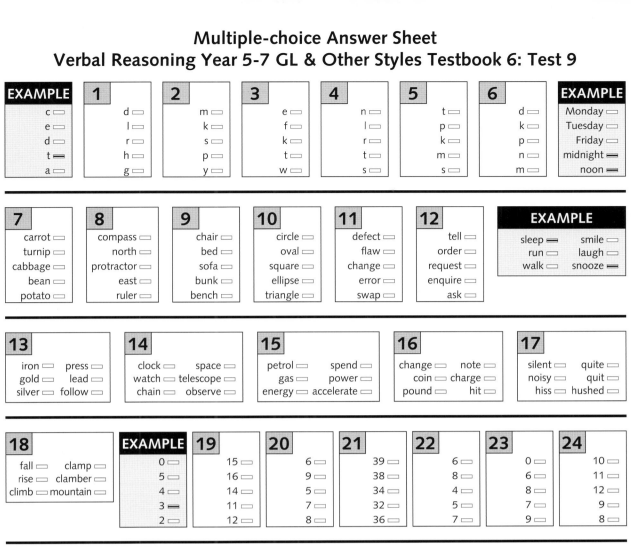

EXAMPLE
- c
- e
- d
- t ▬
- a

1
- d
- l
- r
- h
- g

2
- m
- k
- s
- p
- y

3
- e
- f
- k
- t
- w

4
- n
- l
- r
- t
- s

5
- t
- p
- k
- m
- s

6
- d
- k
- p
- n
- m

EXAMPLE
- Monday
- Tuesday
- Friday
- midnight ▬
- noon ▬

7
- carrot
- turnip
- cabbage
- bean
- potato

8
- compass
- north
- protractor
- east
- ruler

9
- chair
- bed
- sofa
- bunk
- bench

10
- circle
- oval
- square
- ellipse
- triangle

11
- defect
- flaw
- change
- error
- swap

12
- tell
- order
- request
- enquire
- ask

EXAMPLE
- sleep ▬ smile
- run ▬ laugh
- walk ▬ snooze ▬

13
- iron / press
- gold / lead
- silver / follow

14
- clock / space
- watch / telescope
- chain / observe

15
- petrol / spend
- gas / power
- energy / accelerate

16
- change / note
- coin / charge
- pound / hit

17
- silent / quite
- noisy / quit
- hiss / hushed

18
- fall / clamp
- rise / clamber
- climb / mountain

EXAMPLE
- 0
- 5
- 4
- 3 ▬
- 2

19
- 15
- 16
- 14
- 11
- 12

20
- 6
- 9
- 5
- 7
- 8

21
- 39
- 38
- 34
- 32
- 36

22
- 6
- 8
- 4
- 5
- 7

23
- 0
- 6
- 8
- 7
- 9

24
- 10
- 11
- 12
- 9
- 8

EXAMPLE
- The probe
- probe streaked ▬
- streaked through
- through outer
- outer space

25
- Choir members
- members visit
- visit church
- on Sunday
- Sunday mornings

26
- Simon's piano
- piano teacher
- teacher usually
- usually plays
- very well

27
- Mother paid
- paid the
- the old
- old milkman
- milkman yesterday

28
- Many people
- people live
- live near
- that picturesque
- picturesque village

29
- Soldiers never
- never march
- march inside
- inside their
- their barracks

30
- Some magic
- magic ointment
- ointment healed
- healed the
- knight's wounds

31
- A
- B
- C
- D
- E

EXAMPLE
- COLT
- CLAN
- CAST
- COAL
- COLD ▬

32
- BLUSTER
- BLANKET
- BLASTED
- BLADDER
- BLISTER

33
- XJFYFJ
- JXFYFJ
- JXYHFJ
- JXYFYJ
- XYJFYH

34
- PRINT
- PRICE
- PRIZE
- PRIDE
- PRISM

35
- LZDYGFZ
- VPNZYGD
- LZYDGFZ
- PVNZGYD
- PVNZYGD

36
- WALES
- GALES
- WALLS
- WALKS
- GAUGE

37
- KVSGJW
- CNKYAN
- KYTHJW
- CNKYBM
- KVSGIV

EXAMPLE
- GH
- EG
- EF
- FG ▬
- GF

38
- QS
- PR
- RQ
- OS
- QR

39
- RH
- SJ
- SH
- RU
- RG

40
- PO
- OH
- OJ
- PJ
- PI

41
- TD
- SF
- SE
- SD
- RE

42
- LF
- KE
- KG
- ME
- LG

43
- BL
- BO
- EL
- EO
- FL

44
- Jeremy
- Mandy
- Andrew
- Michael
- Joan

EXAMPLE
- prove
- drove ▬
- roped
- rover
- prone

45
- place
- clean
- clamp
- chair
- slack

46
- thief
- feeds
- teach
- teeth
- trace

47
- guide
- blind
- guild
- glide
- bland

48
- nears
- seals
- ruler
- rules
- nurse

49
- chair
- claim
- clamp
- clump
- cramp

50
- vital
- vests
- first
- feast
- fists

Multiple-choice Answer Sheet
Verbal Reasoning Year 5-7 GL & Other Styles Testbook 6: Test 10

EXAMPLE
- c ▬
- l
- i
- m
- b

1
- c
- h
- e
- a
- p

2
- s
- o
- l
- i
- d

3
- w
- i
- t
- e
- r

4
- p
- l
- a
- n
- e

5
- b
- r
- a
- k
- e

6
- p
- l
- a
- c
- e

EXAMPLE
- PAT
- PET
- POT
- PUT ▬
- PIT

7
- TIN
- HAD
- TEN
- TAN
- PIN

8
- ARE
- EAR
- OUR
- HER
- HIS

9
- ATE
- ALE
- EAR
- SEE
- EAT

10
- LEG
- LOG
- RAT
- RAM
- RAG

11
- SIN
- RAY
- ONE
- EYE
- AIM

12
- AND
- END
- HAD
- HID
- BED

EXAMPLE
- up ▬   smile
- run   laugh
- walk   down ▬

13
- start   condemn
- finish   commend
- waste   commence

14
- exchange   pursuit
- sell   perfume
- buy   purchase

15
- wheel   burrow
- lend   borrow
- tunnel   barrow

16
- defeat   lose
- defend   victory
- deflate   winner

17
- contact   touch
- agreed   smash
- contract   expand

18
- yell   hard
- shout   soft
- loud   talk

EXAMPLE
- first   gram
- second ▬   kilo
- third   metre ▬

19
- mention   determine
- tell   found
- said   discover

20
- shot   goal
- kick   penalty
- try   save

21
- drink   leaf
- bean   bag
- cup   golf

22
- thousand   ten
- hundred   twenty
- million   fifty

23
- lock   heavy
- door   wait
- quay   kilo

24
- bulb   brillliant
- sun   excellence
- heavy   superb

EXAMPLE
- 20
- 25
- 40
- 30 ▬
- 35

25
- 23
- 24
- 25
- 26
- 27

26
- 1
- 7
- 9
- 3
- 5

27
- 37
- 32
- 38
- 35
- 36

28
- 26
- 28
- 24
- 23
- 27

29
- 26
- 28
- 29
- 20
- 19

30
- 104
- 102
- 103
- 99
- 101

31
- Rodney
- Albert
- Cassie
- Raquel
- Derek

EXAMPLE
- SU
- WU
- ST
- UV ▬
- VU

32
- IX
- QF
- PE
- IZ
- IY

33
- XZ
- VA
- ZA
- YA
- YZ

34
- PS
- OS
- QT
- QR
- QS

35
- DQ
- HN
- KL
- GM
- RS

36
- AW
- CB
- ZA
- XY
- AX

37
- VW
- WO
- WN
- WP
- WS

EXAMPLE
- motor ▬   engine
- gas   bus
- electric   cycle ▬

38
- fly   them
- bug   hem
- ant   they

39
- on   leap
- off   jump
- in   spring

40
- feat   ring
- deed   her
- dare   full

41
- proper   fed
- tidy   ate
- prim   eat

42
- circle   ruler
- ring   leader
- round   chief

43
- six   ant
- ate   bug
- ten   fly

EXAMPLE
- A
- B
- C ▬
- D
- E

44
- A
- B
- C
- D
- E

45
- A
- B
- C
- D
- E

46
- A
- B
- C
- D
- E

47
- A
- B
- C
- D
- E

48
- A
- B
- C
- D
- E

49
- A
- B
- C
- D
- E

50
- Geoffrey
- Joseph
- Nick
- Susan
- Margaret

Answers

Practice Paper 1

1) p
2) e
3) n
4) d
5) s
6) l
7) August & swim
8) dry & drink
9) neat & warm
10) look & lost
11) angry & annoyed
12) stupid & understand
13) 16
14) 4
15) 96
16) 18
17) 36
18) 43
19) A
20) D
21) E
22) D
23) C
24) B
25) trip & stumble
26) task & job
27) see & view
28) undone & unfinished
29) occupy & inhabit
30) wrong & false
31) D
32) tones
33) pots
34) test
35) mates
36) mat
37) dear
38) Aziz & Mike
39) ea<u>ten</u> today (tent)
40) Spa<u>in to</u>morrow (into)

41) playe<u>rs often</u> (soft)
42) we<u>re ar</u>ranged (rear)
43) puf<u>fin e</u>very (fine)
44) fi<u>re al</u>arm (real)
45) spoon
46) brain
47) climb
48) chair
49) solid
50) march

Practice Paper 2

1) lame & table (b)
2) fair & yearn (y)
3) last & event (e)
4) chat & feast (e)
5) plane & trust (t)
6) able & crumble (c)
7) ARM
8) EAR
9) OIL
10) OUR
11) VAN
12) CAN
13) 24
14) 7
15) 3
16) 13
17) 21
18) 13
19) KM
20) CY
21) KM
22) XH
23) LL
24) VW
25) succeed & fail
26) damp & dry
27) divide & unite
28) raise & lower
29) deep & shallow
30) lead & follow

Answers

31) THIRTY
32) QWSMQY
33) SNAKE
34) ALSLPLLQ
35) PAUSE
36) MIDLAHQ
37) D
38) 18
39) lance & lip
40) rod & bat
41) pots & stab
42) ink & paint
43) blow & pluck
44) word & number
45) 34279
46) 87332442
47) SKATE
48) 174476
49) 17541
50) RESET

Practice Paper 3
1) d
2) e
3) c
4) w
5) h
6) o
7) role & cook
8) banana & pair
9) Australia & Japan
10) base & bottom
11) winner & protractor
12) vague & negative
13) 35
14) 16
15) 48
16) 31
17) 44
18) 22
19) 20
20) 2

21) 3
22) 31
23) 20
24) 4
25) rot & ate
26) in & stance
27) can & not
28) man & hole
29) cast & away
30) time & table
31) C
32) sent
33) seat
34) next
35) trap
36) mean
37) lace
38) SU
39) XY
40) IC
41) YZ
42) NP
43) RU
44) Mary
45) fire
46) duck
47) sink
48) pound
49) correct
50) draw

Practice Paper 4
1) were & shave (h)
2) beat & score or cores (s)
3) bride & rugby (g)
4) pear & quilt (l)
5) what & shine (e)
6) herd & agent (a)
7) TAR
8) HAD
9) TAP
10) NAG

11) LET
12) MEN
13) contain ice (nice)
14) her open (hero/rope)
15) patient's illnesses (sill)
16) spun towards (punt/unto)
17) kite might (item)
18) will improve (limp)
19) QS
20) KH
21) OK
22) EV
23) OS
24) TV
25) 30
26) 16
27) 23
28) 36
29) 130
30) 106
31) PLANE
32) GPINKUJ
33) WORST
34) ORANGE
35) FIXED
36) FACE
37) Jenny
38) D
39) B
40) D
41) E
42) B
43) A
44) B
45) part & role
46) tear & split
47) deceitful & dishonest
48) argue & disagree
49) strand & thread
50) match & contest

Practice Paper 5

1) r
2) t
3) d
4) k
5) m
6) d
7) are about (area)
8) local soldiers (also)
9) runners' tired (stir)
10) tube station (best)
11) this leopard (isle)
12) very early (year)
13) 29
14) 31
15) 12
16) 12
17) 4
18) 18
19) SH
20) KM
21) CP
22) RI
23) LP
24) PQ
25) 1625
26) 4356
27) MATE
28) 87651
29) 97685
30) STEAM
31) 11.20am
32) transparent & opaque
33) steal & meat
34) flew & saw
35) stop & go
36) shell & pod
37) hive & den
38) Andrea & Mohammed
39) tents
40) drama

Answers

41) slide
42) dense
43) train
44) stamp
45) comb & at
46) high & light
47) friend & ship
48) ship & mate
49) rest & ore
50) loud & speaker

Practice Paper 6

1) sock & taxis (t)
2) team & spill or pills (s)
3) rage & crown (n)
4) cater & marker (r)
5) naive & tangle (t)
6) rack & mincer (c)
7) bounce & spring
8) slim & fat
9) first & medicine
10) usual & normal
11) write & draw
12) money & appear
13) 25
14) 14
15) 240
16) 23
17) 11
18) 33
19) 35
20) 23
21) 4
22) 10
23) 15
24) 5
25) GV
26) PW
27) IQ
28) HI
29) HS
30) WY

31) D
32) meal
33) west
34) reef
35) realm
36) cake
37) trap
38) Harry & Katie
39) spotted & seen
40) jump & leap
41) complete & finish
42) laundry & washing
43) crook & criminal
44) box & fight
45) dense
46) trial
47) cried
48) drive
49) brain
50) India

Practice Paper 7

1) inside & exterior
2) dear & cheap
3) rough & smooth
4) backward & forward
5) wild & calm
6) shut & open
7) CON
8) OLD
9) END
10) VAT
11) ALE
12) EVE
13) n
14) e
15) r
16) w
17) f
18) b
19) D
20) C

Answers

21) C
22) B
23) D
24) D
25) 11
26) 14
27) 52
28) 11
29) 28
30) 11
31) MINUTE
32) XTLXNTN
33) BLAME
34) TGSXBPU
35) SLEEP
36) FDOXCZI
37) 3
38) D
39) fresh & polluted
40) grin & scowl
41) all & none
42) human & duck
43) pond & nest
44) hot & cold
45) 3267
46) 7464237
47) STEPS
48) 5472
49) 8422726
50) POTATO

Practice Paper 8
1) best & acute (a)
2) vice & point (o)
3) learn & events (t)
4) pant & blank (l)
5) rage & grind (n)
6) side & flight (l)
7) thin & nest
8) come & dies
9) butter & cup
10) avoid & able

11) back & fire
12) trip & let
13) 4
14) 5
15) 2
16) 5
17) 5
18) 17
19) 36
20) 31
21) 86
22) 40
23) 32
24) 13
25) charge
26) fan
27) point
28) hard
29) flat
30) side
31) B
32) bin
33) tape
34) tame
35) reed
36) rise
37) side
38) 31
39) VA
40) US
41) IN
42) VA
43) KC
44) SC
45) 73425
46) 523645
47) TRADED
48) 16347
49) 739859
50) REMAKE

Answers

Practice Paper 9

1) d
2) p
3) k
4) l
5) k
6) p
7) cabbage & bean
8) north & east
9) bed & bunk
10) square & triangle
11) change & swap
12) tell & order
13) iron & press
14) watch & observe
15) energy & power
16) pound & hit
17) silent & hushed
18) climb & clamber
19) 11
20) 8
21) 34
22) 5
23) 0
24) 8
25) vis<u>it ch</u>urch (itch)
26) pia<u>no tea</u>cher (note)
27) milk<u>man y</u>esterday (many)
28) picturesqu<u>e vil</u>lage (evil)
29) mar<u>ch in</u>side (chin)
30) magi<u>c oin</u>tment (coin)
31) C
32) BLASTED
33) JXYFYJ
34) PRICE
35) VPNZYGD
36) WALES
37) KVSGIV
38) QR
39) RU
40) OH

41) RE
42) LF
43) EL
44) Jeremy
45) clean
46) teach
47) blind
48) nurse
49) claim
50) feast

Practice Paper 10

1) chap & shine (e)
2) sold & brain (i)
3) water & claim (i)
4) lane & spell (p)
5) baked & bread (r)
6) paces & slides (l)
7) TAN
8) OUR
9) EAT
10) RAG
11) RAY
12) AND
13) finish & commence
14) sell & purchase
15) lend & borrow
16) defeat & victory
17) contract & expand
18) loud & soft
19) said & found
20) try & goal
21) bean & leaf
22) hundred & ten
23) quay & wait
24) heavy & brilliant
25) 23
26) 9
27) 38
28) 27
29) 19
30) 99

31) Albert
32) IX
33) YZ
34) QT
35) GM
36) AW
37) WO
38) ant & hem
39) off & spring
40) feat & her
41) prim & ate
42) ring & leader
43) ten & ant
44) A
45) C
46) A
47) B
48) C
49) C
50) Susan

PROGRESS CHARTS

	Total Score	**Percentage**
Test 1		%
Test 2		%
Test 3		%
Test 4		%
Test 5		%
Test 6		%
Test 7		%
Test 8		%
Test 9		%
Test 10		%

Overall Percentage | **%** | For the average add up % and divide by 10

CERTIFICATE OF

ACHIEVEMENT

This certifies

_____

has successfully completed

11+ Verbal Reasoning
Year 5–7
TESTBOOK **6**

Overall percentage
score achieved

%

Comment _____

_____

Signed _____
(teacher/parent/guardian)

Date _____